ELE

COM

by

R. A. PENFOLD

**BERNARD BABANI (publishing) LTD
THE GRAMPIANS
SHEPHERDS BUSH ROAD
LONDON W6 7NF
ENGLAND**

PLEASE NOTE

Although every care has been taken with the production of this book to ensure that any projects, designs, modifications and/or programs etc. contained herewith, operate in a correct and safe manner and also that any components specified are normally available in Great Britain, the Publishers do not accept responsibility in any way for the failure, including fault in design, of any project, design, modification or program to work correctly or to cause damage to any other equipment that it may be connected to or used in conjunction with, or in respect of any other damage or injury that may be so caused, nor do the Publishers accept responsibility in any way for the failure to obtain specified components.

Notice is also given that if equipment that is still under warranty is modified in any way or used or connected with home-built equipment then that warranty may be void.

© 1986 BERNARD BABANI (publishing) LTD

First Published – November 1986

British Library Cataloguing in Publication Data
Penfold, R.A.
    Electronic circuits for the computer
    control of robots.
    1. Robots——Data processing
    2. Microcomputers
    I. Title
    629.8'92   TJ211

ISBN 0 85934 153 4

Printed and Bound in Great Britain by Cox & Wyman Ltd, Reading

CONTENTS

Preface

The term robot tends to conjure up images of large (usually) humanoid machines capable of walking, talking, and many other human activities. With modern technology robots are now very much in the realms of reality rather than science fiction, but the real thing bears little resemblance to the Hollywood fantasy. Most robots are either large industrial types which are static and of the arm variety, or small educational/hobbyist devices which are either simplified and scaled down arm designs, or vehicles of the so called "buggy" or "turtle" variety.

Although real robots may not be as tantalising as their fictional counterparts they represent one of the most interesting fields for electronics hobbyists and experimenters. It is possible to buy ready-made robots at low cost these days, but the do it yourself approach probably offers greater scope for originality and consequently offers greater and more lasting interest value. The mechanics of robotics do not represent too much of a problem as there are robotics kits and a wide range of mechanical components available for those who do not have the facilities or the inclination to tackle this aspect from scratch. The microcontroller is not too much of a problem either, since the software need not be terribly complex and many inexpensive home computers are well suited to the task. Ideally the computer should have a user port or some other form of parallel port (either built-in or as an add-on board), but with a little extra electronics a standard RS232C or RS423 serial type will suffice.

Probably the main stumbling block for most would-be robot builders is the electronics to interface the computer to the motors, and the sensors which provide feedback from the robot to the computer. The purpose of this book is to provide some electronic circuits which bridge this gap. Ideally the reader should have some basic background knowledge of electronics, but none of the circuits are very complex and they are well within the capabilities of near beginners.

R. A. Penfold

Chapter 1

MOTOR CONTROL

Robots may vary greatly in their degree of sophistication, the facilities they offer, and their intended applications, but they are all basically one or more computer controlled motors of one kind or another. It is largely the mechanics of the system and any sensors that determine just what the robot can and can not do. Of course, the hardware is really only half the system, and the software is equally important to the success or failure of the system, and in deciding its precise function.

In this chapter we will consider the control of various types of electric motor, including small DC types, mains powered motors, stepper motors, and simple solenoids. At this stage we will not be deeply concerned with the mechanics or software of the system. and these are matters that will be dealt with in more detail in subsequent chapters.

DC Motors
Probably the most popular type of electric motor for use in simple home constructed robots is the ordinary low voltage DC type, as used in many model boats, cars, etc. These are readily available from some model shops as well as from some electronic component suppliers. Some robotics kits are available, and these usually contain two or three DC motors plus a range of other useful mechanical parts including gears, wheels and drive components. These are consequently very useful for anyone wishing to experiment with simple and inexpensive robots, and certainly represent an excellent starting point. Of course, in most cases these kits are intended for producing manually controlled robots, but with a little ingenuity it is not usually too difficult to convert them to computer control. Also, they can simply be used as a source of useful parts rather than complete models if preferred.

These motors usually consist of two permanent magnets and an armature with three electromagnets which are driven in a simple series or parallel arrangement, giving just two electrical connections to the motor. As far as controlling them is concerned, the speed is dependent on the voltage supplied to the motor, and the direction is controlled by the polarity of the supply. If simple on/off switching is all that is required, control from a computer output port can be very simple indeed. One way of tackling things is to use some form of solid state switching to drive the motor, or the alternative of switching via a relay can be adopted. A relay is merely a mechanical switch which is operated via an electromagnet, and although this may seem to be a rather old fashioned way of doing things in these days of complex solid state electronic devices, there are advantages to this form of switching, and relays do not seem to be waning at all in popularity.

Computer Ports

In order to understand any type of computer control there are a few fundamentals of computing which must be understood first. There is insufficient space available here to give a detailed description of computer interfacing techniques, but some of the more important basics of the subject will be covered. Those who are already familiar with computer interfacing should skip over this section, while those who are not should try to grasp the points covered here before trying to interface any circuits to their computer. There are books which provide further information on computer interfacing, including Book No. BP130, *Micro Interfacing Circuits – Book 1* and Book No. BP131, *Micro Interfacing Circuits – Book 2* from the same publisher and author as this publication.

Virtually every computer has some form of expansion port, but it is not usually possible to directly take signals from these which can be used with electric motors and other devices. Some form of add-on board is required, and for our purposes a PIA (parallel interface adaptor) board is the most suitable. Some computers do have a suitable built-in port in the form of a user port, and the Commodore 64 and BBC machines are two examples of computers which fall into this category. It is often possible to use a Centronics type parallel printer port as an output to drive simple add-ons, and a port of this type can usually provide one or two inputs as well, but a reasonable knowledge of your computer's hardware would be needed in order to use its printer port as a general purpose digital port. It would obviously be unwise to experiment with expensive computer equipment unless you have a reasonable understanding of what you are doing.

With most general purpose parallel interfaces it is not normally a matter of having some input lines and some separate output lines. A more common arrangement is to have a number of lines which can be set as inputs or as outputs, as required. In some cases each individual line can be set as an input or an output, but in others there might be (say) 16 lines divided into two groups of 8, with each group having to be set as all inputs or all outputs. If your computer has a built-in user port of some kind then the manual should give at least basic details on how to set it up and use it, or there should be an advanced manual or other publication which gives details of this. If you obtain an add-on parallel interface for your computer then this should certainly be supplied with some form of documentation giving concise information on how to set up and use the unit.

As a typical example of a parallel port which illustrates some fundamental points very well, we will consider the user port of the BBC model B computer (the B+, B+128, and Master series computers are all fitted with exactly the same port). Figure 1 shows the lines available on this user port, and one row is devoted to only the ground (earth or negative supply rail) and +5 volt supply rail. The inclusion of a 5 volt supply output is a common feature of user and parallel ports, and a very useful one as it often eliminates the need for any add-ons connected to the port to have their own power supply. However, bear in mind that there is a limit to the amount of power that can be tapped off from the computer. With the BBC model B, assuming that the power port is not being used to power disc drives, a generous 1.25 amps is

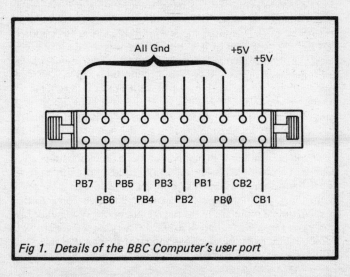

Fig 1. Details of the BBC Computer's user port

available, but most other computers can only provide about a tenth of this current level. Sometimes other supply voltages are available from the computer, and although the user port provides only the +5 volt output, the power port additionally furnishes +12 and −5 volt outputs. Again, there is a limit to the current than can be taken from any additional supply outputs, and in this case the relevant figures are 1.25 amps and 50 milliamps. It is especially important to bear in mind the limitations of power supply outputs in an application such as robotics where quite high currents can be involved. In general the computer will be able to support any electronics that are connected to the user or other form of parallel port, but devices such as solenoids and electric motors may well require too much current and in most instances will require a separate power source.

Lines CB1 and CB2 are what are termed "handshake" lines, and they are designed for use in regulating the flow of data into or out of the user port. In a robotics application they will often be of little value, although CB2 can be used as a general purpose output if desired (CB1 can only function as an input). Using these lines is something less than completely straightforward, and it is not a subject which will be covered here.

The lines of most interest in the present context are PB0 to PB7, and these are general purpose inputs and outputs. The BBC user port is very versatile, and each line is individually programmable as an input or an output. The data direction register is used to set each line to the required mode, and this register is at address &FE62. Setting a bit of this register to 0 sets the corresponding user port line as an input, setting a bit to 1 sets the relevant user port line as an output. At switch-on all the bits of this register are set to 0, and all the lines therefore start out as inputs. This is a common arrangement, and it is a sort of simple safety measure. If any outputs are connected to the user port it ensures that at switch-on they are driving inputs, and the potentially disastrous situation where outputs are driving outputs is avoided.

If you are familiar with binary arithmetic the explanation given above is probably sufficient for you to be able to set up the user port lines as inputs and (or) outputs, as desired. If binary is something you have not yet encountered, then some further explanation is required. In the binary numbering system there are only two single digit numbers; 0 and 1. This is a convenient way of doing things from the electronic point of view in that these two numbers can easily be represent by an electronic circuit, with a low voltage of typically around 0 to 0.8 volts corresponding to 0 (often called "logic 0" or just "low"), and a higher voltage of around 2.5 to 5 volts corresponding to 1 ("logic 1" or "high").

A detailed explanation of the binary numbering system would be out of place here, and really all that is needed is a basic understanding of how decimal numbers relate to binary numbers, which then makes it easy to understand the relationship between decimal numbers and the logic states on the user port lines that they produce. Here things are simplified by the fact that we are only dealing with eight bit (Binary digIT) numbers as there are only eight user port lines. This gives a binary number range of 00000000 to 11111111, which is equivalent to a range of 0 to 255 in the ordinary decimal numbering system.

In effect, a binary digit set at 0 contributes 0 to the total value, while a bit which is set at 1 corresponds to a particular decimal number, and contributes that number to the total value. Working from the extreme right hand column towards the left, the numbers are 1, 2, 4, 8, 16, etc. The list shown below gives the number to which each user port line corresponds:-

PB0	1	PB4	16
PB1	2	PB5	32
PB2	4	PB6	64
PB3	8	PB7	128

Relating this to the data direction register and the value to be written to it to provide the required set of input/output lines, it is just a matter of deciding which lines are to be outputs, looking up the corresponding numbers for these lines in the above list, and then writing the total of these numbers to the data direction register. As a simple example, assume that PB0 to PB3 are to be set as outputs and that the other four lines are to be inputs. Looking up the numbers for PB0 to PB3 in the list gives 1, 2, 4, and 8, which gives a total of 15. This is the value that would be written to the data direction register, and with BBC BASIC this would be done with the command:-

$$?\&FE62=15$$

The BBC machine is unusual in that a question mark ("?") is used ahead of a number to indicate that it is an address. With most other 6502 based computers (or types with a 6502 bus compatible microprocessor) the POKE instruction is used to write values to output devices. With Z80 based computers it is usually the OUT command that must be used. In the majority of cases the user port lines are either all set as inputs, or are all set up as outputs, which requires data direction register values of 0 and 255 respectively.

It is important to realise that the data direction register is only used for setting up the user port with the desired combination of input and output lines, and that data is not read from or written to the port at this address. The peripheral register, which can be regarded as the user port lines, is at address FE60. This register can be read with the instruction:-

PRINT ?&FE60

If a line is low it contributes zero to the returned value. If a line is high, the number contributed to the returned value depends on the line concerned, and can be found by refering to the list provided earlier (e.g. PB7 adds 128 to the returned value when it is set high). With all the lines left in their default (input) state, trying the instruction given above will provide an answer of 255, since the inputs have pull-up resistors which take them high if they are simply left floating.

Taking in data from sensors of a robot is often a crucial part of robotics, but for the moment we are more concerned about writing data to the user port than reading from it. Writing 0 to a bit of the peripheral register sets the corresponding user port line low – writing a 1 to a bit of the peripheral register sets the appropriate line high. This does, of course, assume that the line concerned has first been set as an output, and data written to lines set as inputs has no effect. Looking at things in the most simple possible terms, the correct value to write to the peripheral register can be calculated by first deciding which lines are to be set high, looking up the values for these in the list given previously, and then adding up the numbers to give the total value to be written to the peripheral register. In other words it is the same as calculating the value to be written to the data direction register, but it is lines being set high instead of lines being designated as outpus in this case. As a simple example, to set PB4 to PB7 all high with the other lines being set low, a value of 240 would be needed (16+32+64+128=240).

Relay Control

The ability to switch output lines between 0 volts or so and around

3 to 5 volts does not permit the direct control of small electric motors. On the face of it this should be possible, since a low voltage of about one volt or less is inadequate to cause most small electric motors to operate at all, whereas about 3 to 5 volts will properly drive some of the lower voltage types. The problem is simply that the user port output lines (and those of any comparable port) are only intended for driving digital inputs on add-on circuits, and have only a modest current drive capability. The precise drive current depends on the particular device used to provide the output lines, but would typically only be a few milliamps with one of the lines short circuited to one or other of the supply rails. Small electric motors require around one hundred times this current level, and with the output being loaded down by no more than about 20 to 30% so as to leave an adequate drive voltage.

A relay represents the most simple means of controlling an electric motor from a digital output, but in most cases the relay can not be directly driven from the output lines. Again, it is a matter of insufficient drive current being available, although in this case the current requirement is somewhat less, with a typical low voltage relay requiring a drive current of only about 40 milliamps for reliable operation. There are in fact some relays that can be directly driven from the types of digital output that have relatively high drive currents, but the relay contacts mostly have inadequate ratings to be of any real use in this application. Relay contact ratings are something that has to be carefully watched when driving an inductive load such as a solenoid or an electric motor, as under these circumstances the maximum permissible current and voltage ratings are generally substantially less than for resistive loads. When a solenoid is activated or deactivated there is a tendency for the rapidly changing magetic field to generate a fairly high voltage across the coil, and this voltage can lead to contact sparking at the switch or relay contacts. This tends to cause corrosion and a high contact resistance when the contacts are closed, and in an extreme case it is even possible for the contacts to become welded together. I would therefore strongly recommend the use of a relay with generous contact ratings when driving any highly inductive load.

The circuit shown in Figure 2 enables a relay to be controlled from a digital output, and in order to control several motors it is merely necessary to use several of these circuits driven from separate digital output lines. Transistor Tr1 operates as a

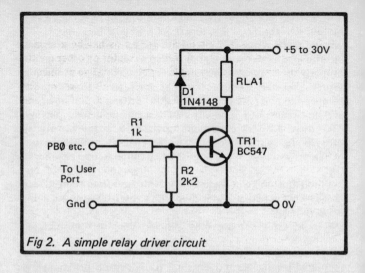

Fig 2. A simple relay driver circuit

straightforward common emitter amplifier/switch which is switched on when the input line goes high, R1 and R2 act as a potential divider which ensures that the base voltage fed to Tr1 when the input is in the low state is not sufficient to bias the device into conduction and hold the relay switched on. D1 is the protection diode which is almost invariably included when a semiconductor switching device is used to control a highly inductive load. It was pointed out earlier that a high voltage can be generated across a solenoid when it is switched off, due to the magnet force around the coil rapidly decaying and inducing the voltage in the coil. With a mechanical switch this gives the problem of sparking at the contacts, but with semiconductor switching it is more a problem of instant destruction of the switching device, and possibly of other semiconductor components in the circuit as well. The voltage spike is at a fairly high impedance and of opposite polarity to the supply and D1 has the effect of virtually short circuiting the pulse, clipping it at an innocuous 0.6 volts or so. The high source impedance of the pulse ensures that D1 does not receive a fatally high pulse of current. Do not be tempted to omit protection diodes such as D1, since this would almost certainly result in the switching device being short lived, and it could just possibly result in expensive damage to other components in the system. Semiconductor devices are very intollerant of even moderately high voltages for even very short periods of time.

The relay and driver circuit are shown as having a separate power supply in Figure 2, but if the computer or other controlling circuit can provide a suitable supply voltage at an adequate current then this can be used. In many cases the controlling equipment will only provide a 5 volt supply output, and this is rather restrictive in that there are few readily available relays that are guaranteed to operate properly with such a low supply voltage. Some relays which have a nominal operating voltage of 6 volts have a minimum operating voltage of about 4.7 or 4.8 volts, and this makes them just about suitable for operation on a nominal 5 volt supply. The coil resistance is an important factor to keep in mind, and in general, the higher this resistance the better. A high resistance has the advantage of giving a relatively low level of current consumption (the current drain is equal to the supply voltage divided by the coil resistance). A 12 volt type with a 1200 ohm coil would therefore have a current consumption of only around 10 milliamps (0.01 amps), but a 12 volt 120 ohm coil would take some 100 milliamps 0.1 amps). This factor is especially important where a circuit has several relays, as types having a low coil resistance could result in the circuit drawing a massive supply current under worst case conditions (with all the relays switched on). It is generally easier to locate suitable medium – high resistance relays than to provide the system with a large and expensive power supply. The BC547 specified for Tr1 can handle supply currents of up to 100 milliamps, and it should not be necessary to have higher currents than this (although it could be changed for a higher current type (such as the 500 milliamp BC337) if necessary.

The 30 volt maximum supply voltage is imposed by the maximum collector to emitter voltage rating of Tr1, but again, this should be more than adequate, although Tr1 could be made a high voltage type if necessary. Most relays will operate over a fairly wide coil voltage range with the maximum often being two to three times the nominal operating voltage, but it is best to have a supply voltage at something not too far removed from the nominal figure. This keeps the power consumption of the relay within reasonable bounds.

There are a number of reed relays available, and at first sight, with their modest coil voltage and current requirements, these can seem to be ideal for robotics applications. Unfortunately, this type of relay usually only has very low contact ratings, especially when used with inductive loads, and this makes them unsuitable for our purposes.

Contacts
The relay provides a mechanical switching action of some kind, and there are two basic types. These are the straightforward on/off type, and changeover contacts. Most relays these days seem to have changeover contacts, and this is sensible as these can replace simple on/off types, but the latter can not be used in place of changeover contacts. Some relays only have one set of contacts, but most types have two or four sets.

For straightforward on/off switching of an electric motor the simple set up of Figure 3 is all that is needed. The relay contacts are shown as changeover types with one terminal ignored so that

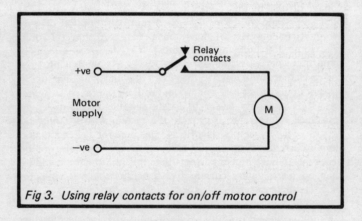

Fig 3. Using relay contacts for on/off motor control

the required on/off switching action is obtained. This is the way you will most probably need to do things, but obviously a set of true on/off contacts could be used instead.

In most applications it is not just on/off control that is required, and direction control is also needed. To alter the direction of the motor it is merely necessary to reverse the supply, and this can be achieved using twin changeover contacts in the arrangement shown in Figure 4. Note that it is not possible to use a single relay for both on/off and direction control, and that two relays controlled from separate output lines are required.

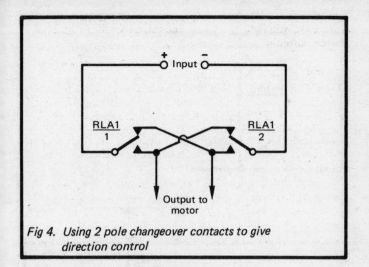

Fig 4. *Using 2 pole changeover contacts to give direction control*

Semiconductor Control

Controlling a motor via relays has the advantage of complete isolation between the controlling circuit and the motor, and provided the normal safety precautions are observed, relay control is perfectly usable with AC mains motors, or any type of load in fact (provided it is within the relay's contact ratings of course). Semiconductor switches are a viable alternative though, particularly with low voltage DC loads which can be controlled by ordinary transistors.

One way of tackling the problem is to use a circuit of the type shown in Figure 1 and described previously, but to connect the electric motor in place of the relay. The original circuit is not really suitable in most cases as the electric motor will require more current that the BC547 can provide. With a motor that draws a few hundred milliamps or more (which most do when under moderate load) there is also the problem that the amplification provided by Tr1 might be inadequate to drive the motor properly, even if Tr1 is swopped for a type which has an adequate current rating.

Better results can be obtained using a VMOS transistor in the manner shown in Figure 5(a). VMOS transistors are a form of power field effect device, and they are enhancement mode transistors. In other words, whereas most field effect transistors

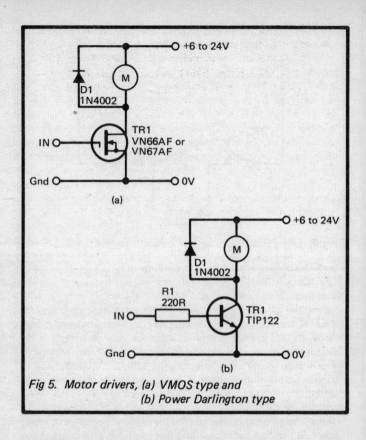

*Fig 5. Motor drivers, (a) VMOS type and
(b) Power Darlington type*

normally conduct heavily and require a reverse bias to switch them off (depletion mode operation), VMOS types are more like ordinary biploar transistors in that they are normally cut off and will only pass minute leakage currents, and a forward bias is required in order to bring them into conduction. Another important difference between VMOS transistors and most other field effect types is that they have a very low resistance when they are switched on. This drain to source resistance is typically only one or two ohms, which compares with around one or two hundred ohms for a normal MOS or junction gate field effect transistor. Like other forms of field effect transistor, VMOS types have an extremely high input resistance of many megohms and require very little input current. In fact they are best regarded as voltage rather than current operated.

When using any semiconductor switching device you must always bear in mind that, unlike the mechanical switch contacts of a relay, a significant voltage drop occurs through the device. This voltage drop is not normally very large at typically about one volt or so, but even with a 12 volt electric motor this can cause a noticeable reduction in power, and with lower voltage types the power loss can be quite large. Ideally the supply voltage should therefore be increased by a volt or two in order to compensate for this voltage drop.

Also bear in mind that like relay contacts and other forms of switch, semiconductor switching elements have voltage and current limits which should not be exceeded. In the case of the VN66AF and VN67AF devices these limits are 60 volts and 2 amps respectively. In this case where only a modest gate voltage is used to turn the device on it would probably be better to regard 1 amp as the maximum usable drain current.

Although VMOS transistors are obviously a form of MOS transistor, the VN66AF and VN67AF do not require the usual antistatic handling precautions as they have a built-in zener protection diode connected between the gate and source terminals.

Darlington Driver
A Darlington Pair makes a good alternative to a VMOS device, and this is two transistors connected to effectively provide a single ultra-high gain device. These can be made from two separate devices, but these days Darlington power devices are readily available, and it is easier to use one of these. Figure 5(b) shows how a device of this type can be used as a motor driver. The TIP122 has a maximum collector current rating of 5 amps, but with the limited drive current available in this case it would be advisable not to use the circuit with loads that require more than about 2 amps or so. This is not really a very great restriction, since most low voltage DC motors draw a current of less than 2 amps even when loaded quite heavily. The maximum emitter–collector voltage rating for the TIP122 is 100 volts. However, with any semiconductor device it is advisable to stay comfortably within its voltage ratings. Again, this is not a great restriction since in most cases the motor's operating voltage will be 12 volts or less, and is unlikely to be greater than 24 volts.

Although these two circuits can switch quite high powers, the power dissipated in the switching device is not very great. The device is either cut off and passing no significant current, or it is switched hard on so that there is little voltage present across the device. With the device switched on and passing high currents there is a significant amount of power dissipated in it, as even with a voltage of only about 1 volt dropped through the component, this still amounts to one or two watts with an amp or two of collector current. A power device can normally dissipate a watt or so perfectly safely without the aid of a heatsink, but if the device is switching high currents it is probably best to play safe and fit it with a small finned heatsink. Ready made types are readily available, or an adequate heatsink can be home constructed by bending a small piece of 16 swg aluminium into a "U" shape and drilling it with a 4 millimetre diameter hole for the mounting bolt.

Direction Control
There is no true semiconductor equivalent to a mechanical changeover contact arrangement, but it is possible to use two semiconductor switches to give much the same effect, and motor direction control is possible using four semiconductor switches to give a simulated two pole chageover contact arrangement. The circuit diagram of Figure 6 shows how this can be achieved.

If we just concentrate on the output stage for the moment (Tr3 to Tr6), those who are familiar with audio amplifier circuits will probably find this quite familiar. If we take Tr3 and Tr4, these are connected in the standard complementary class B audio amplifier output circuit. They both operate as emitter followers, but in this application they perform as switches rather than in a linear mode. The bases are therefore only stable when at virtually the full positive supply voltage or at virtually zero volts, and they are never held between these two extremes.

With the bases taken to something approaching the full supply voltage, assuming that the load is connected between the emitters and the negative supply rail, Tr3 drives the load while Tr4 is cut off and plays no active roll in the circuit. With the bases taken to the 0 volt supply rail Tr3 and Tr4 both become switched off, and no significant current is supplied to the load. If, on the other hand, the load is connected between the two emitters and the positive supply rail, it will be supplied with current by Tr3 when the bases are at the negative supply potential, and switched off when the bases are taken fully positive. In order to give direction control a

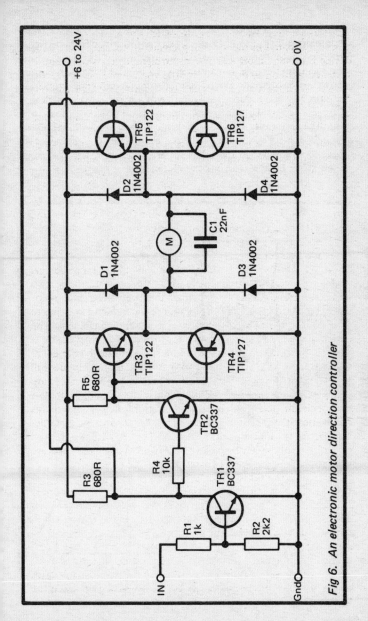

Fig 6. An electronic motor direction controller

15

single ended output stage is insufficient, and the second complementary output stage with the motor driven from between the two outputs is required. This is essentially the same as the bridge amplifiers used in audio applications where a high output power is needed and only a limited supply voltage is available. Figure 7(a) and Figure 7(b) help to explain the way in which this bridge arrangement functions. An important point to note here is that the two sets of base terminals must be driven with antiphase signals if the circuit is to give the required action (i.e. if one set of bases are taken high the other set are taken low, and reversing their states reverses the motor's direction).

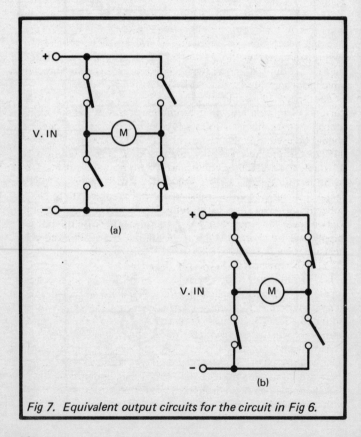

Fig 7. Equivalent output circuits for the circuit in Fig 6.

Figure 7(a) shows the effective circuit with the bases of Tr3 and Tr4 taken high, and the bases of Tr5 and Tr6 taken low. The motor is connected across the supply rails via Tr3 and Tr6, with the other two output devices being cut off. Figure 7(b) shows the effective circuit with the states of the input signals reversed, and this time it is Tr4 and Tr5 that connect the motor across the supply rails, with Tr3 and Tr6 being cut off and playing no active part in the circuit. The important point to note here is that the terminal of the motor which connects to the positive supply rail in Figure 7(a) is connected to the negative supply rail in Figure 7(b). Thus the circuit provides the required supply reversal and direction control.

Returning to Figure 6, Tr1 operates as a simple common emitter inverter stage, and the main purpose of this is to ensure that the drive signal to Tr5 and Tr6 switches between the full supply voltage even though the input signal might only switch between about 0.8 and 25 volts. Tr2 acts as a second inverter which provides the antiphase drive signal for Tr3 and Tr4.

The specified output transistors are adequate for output currents of up to a few hundred milliamps (say about 400 milliamps), but for higher currents Darlington Pair power devices should be used. Suitable types are TIP122 for Tr3 and Tr5, and TIP127 for Tr4 and Tr6. For currents of 1 amp or more it is advisable to fit all four output transistors with small heatsinks, or to fit all four devices onto a single medium size heatsink. The metal heat-tabs of these transistors connect internally to their collector terminals, and it is therefore important to use insulation kits on them if a single heatsink is used, as otherwise the power supply will be short circuit via the output transistors and the heatsink. Use a continuity checker to ensure that the insulation is effective before applying power to the circuit.

D1 to D4 are protection diodes, and C1 is a suppression capacitor. The latter can help to reduce problems with the motor generating radio frequency interference, and for it to have optimum effect C1 should be mounted direct across the terminals of the motor rather than with the rest of the circuit.

An advantage of this method of control when compared with relay control is that it is instantaneous, and it is also reliable in that there are no moving parts to wear out. Its main disadvantage is that there is a volt or so dropped across each output device, and with two devices in series with the motor this gives a total voltage loss of around 3 volts. The supply voltage therefore needs to be about 3 volts higher than the required output voltage to the motor. Relays are very hard wearing and reliable these days, and for this type of application they are my preferred way of doing things, but probably most constructors prefer to use a semiconductor switching circuit such as this one.

Components for Direction Controller (Fig. 6).
Resistors, ¼ watt 5% carbon film except where noted

R1	1k
R2	2k2
R3	680R 1W
R4	10k
R5	680R 1W

Capacitor

C1	22nF ceramic

Semiconductors

Tr1	BC337
Tr2	BC337
Tr3	TIP122
Tr4	TIP127
Tr5	TIP122
Tr6	TIP127
D1 to D4	1N4002 (4 off)

Miscellaneous
Circuit board, heatsink, wire, etc.

Single-Ended Controller
It is possible to obtain direction control using a single- ended semiconductor driver circuit, and this type of circuit has the advantage of only placing a single transistor in series with the motor. Apart from reducing power losses, having one rather than two devices in series with the motor gives better speed stability (a subject which will be considered in some detail later in this chapter). The disadvantage of a single ended driver is that it requires the use of dual balanced power supplies. Figure 8 shows the circuit for a simple motor driver of this type.

The output stage is essentially the same as that which was used in each section of the bridge in Figure 6, and is a simple complementary emitter follower type. Here though, there are

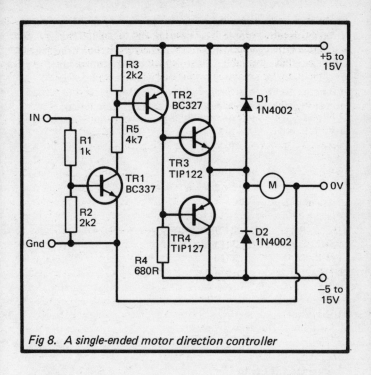

Fig 8. A single-ended motor direction controller

dual supplies, with each one being a volt or two more than the required output voltage. Thus if the motor is a 6 volt type, supplies of around plus and minus 7 or 7.5 volts would be needed (not plus and minus 3.5 volts giving a total supply potential of 7 volts). With the bases of Tr3 and Tr4 taken to the positive supply potential Tr3 supplies power to the motor from the positive supply, and Tr4 becomes cut off. Taking the bases to the full negative supply potential results in Tr4 driving the motor from the negative supply rail while Tr3 is switched off. Therefore the polarity of the supply to the motor is controlled by the input signal to the bases of Tr3 and Tr4, and the required direction control is obtained.

Tr2 is a common emitter driver stage which ensures that the output stage is driven with suitably high input voltages. Tr1 interfaces Tr2 properly to the 5 volt logic input signal levels. A high input signal switches on Tr1, Tr2 and Tr3 so that the motor is driven from the positive supply. A low input level cuts off these three transistors but switches on Tr4 so that the motor is driven from the negative supply. The motor is wired up to the circuit with the polarity that gives the desired direction of rotation from a high input level (as with any DC motor direction control circuit).

Components for Dual Supply Version (Fig. 8).
Resistors, all ¼ watt 5% carbon film except where noted.

R1	1k
R2	2k2
R3	2k2
R4	680R 2W
R5	4k7

Semiconductors

Tr1	BC337
Tr2	BC327
Tr3	TIP122
Tr4	TIP127
D1	1N4002
D2	1N4002

Miscellaneous
Circuit board, heatsink, wire, etc.

Adding On/Off Control
So far we have considered on/off and direction control separately, but most applications require that both types of control are available. With relay control there is no difficulty, and the motor is just fed from the direction control contacts by way of the contacts which provide the on/off switching. Things are also quite easy with a mixture of semiconductor and relay control, but are less straightforward with all semiconductor control. If this type of control is required, then it is best to use a direction control circuit of the type shown in Figure 6 (and discussed previously) in conjunction with the on/off switching circuit of Figure 9.

The advantage of this circuit over a simple common emitter switch is that it does not place the switching element in the earth (negative) supply rail. This is not always of great importance, but in some circumstances it can be crucial, particularly where the motor is not being driven from a supply output of the computer or other controlling circuit. Problems with earthing can then result in

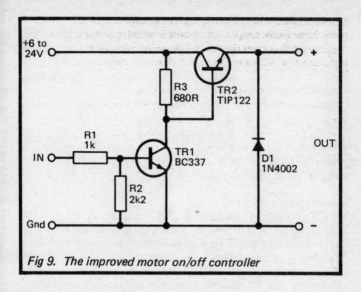

Fig 9. The improved motor on/off controller

the switching transistor being bypassed so that the motor is permanently switched on. This problem is totally eliminated with the circuit of Figure 9.

The circuit is very straightforward in operation. With the input low, Tr1 is cut off and emitter follower output transistor Tr2 is biased hard into conduction by R3. With the input taken high, Tr1 is biased hard into conduction, taking the base of Tr2 low and cutting off the output. Note that there is a voltage drop of about 1.5 volts through Tr2 (in addition to any voltage drops through the direction control circuit), and the the supply input voltage must be chosen to take this into account. With supply currents of about 1 amp or more Tr2 will operate quite warm, and it is advisable to fit it with a small heatsink.

As the circuit stands, a high input level switches the motor off, and a low level activates it. This may seem to be a slightly illogical way of having things, but with computer control it does not really matter which logic level switches the motor on and which logic state switches it off. The software is simply written to suit the hardware. However, if you would prefer the opposite method of control it is merely necessary to add an inverter at the input of the circuit.

Components for Improved On/Off Controller (Fig. 9)
Resistors, all ¼ watt 5% carbon film except where noted.

R1	1k
R2	2k2
R3	680R 2W

Semiconductors

Tr1	BC337
Tr2	TIP 122
D1	1N4002

Miscellaneous
Circuit board, heatsink, wire, etc.

Speed Control
In most robotics applications a single motor speed is all that is required, but in some fairly advanced applications it can be advantageous to slow down the motor. A typical example would be a robot arm and clasper arrangement where very delicate manoeuvering is required in order to grasp a small or fragile object, but once the object has been picked up it is advantageous to have faster movements so that the unit is not tediously slow in operation. One way of tackling the problem is to use a high quality digital to analogue converter to produce a programmable output voltage which can then be used to drive the motor via a suitable voltage/buffer amplifier. Using a standard 8 bit digital to analogue converter this gives stop plus 255 different speeds, although in practice many of the lower voltages would probably not be sufficient to turn the motor. This would almost certainly still give in excess of 100 different usable speed settings. In practice it is difficult to envisage a situation where such precise speed control would be needed. It would not be necessary to use all the speeds of course, but this would then be a very wasteful way of tackling things. Not only due to the expense of a high quality analogue to digital converter, but because eight output lines would be tied up in just controlling the speed of the motor. This is fine if you have a couple of dozen output lines or more available, but not if you are restricted to an eight bit (plus handshake lines) user port.

For most purposes a choice of seven speeds plus an "off" setting is more than adequate, and this is something that can be accomplished under the control of just three output lines. Figure 10 shows a suitable circuit, and this is based on a 4051BE CMOS eight way analogue switch (IC1).

If we start by considering the function of IC1, this has eight input terminals and one output terminal. It has three control inputs, and it is the binary pattern on these which determines which input is fed through to the output. For example, 000 selects input '0', 001 selects input '1', 010 selects input '2', and so on. Although we are talking here in terms of the device having eight inputs and one output, it gives a true analogy of a mechanical eight way switch, and it is genuinely bilateral. In other words, it can be used to select one of eight input signals and feed it through to the output, or it can feed an input signal on the "common" terminal through to one of the eight outputs.

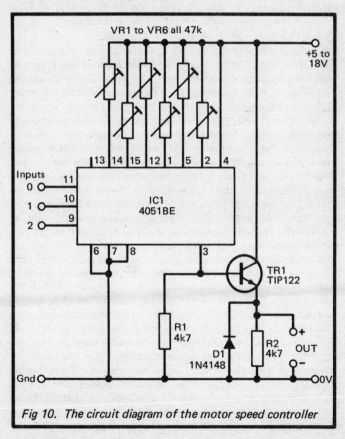

Fig 10. The circuit diagram of the motor speed controller

The device has an "inhibit" input, but this is not required in this application and this terminal is simply tied to the 0 volt supply rail. There is also a third supply input which can be used in applications where the circuit has dual supplies and the switches must operate at voltages negative of the 0 volt rail. Again, this is of no importance in this application where there is no negative supply rail, and the relevant terminal of IC1 is simply connected to the 0 volt supply rail. There are two respects in which CMOS analogue switches differ from the mechanical counterparts, and one of these is their much higher "on" resistance of around one or two hundred ohms. The other is that the signal voltages should not stray significantly outside the supply rail limits. Neither of these restrictions poses a major problem in this application.

Looking at the operation of the speed control circuit now, Tr1 is an emitter follower buffer stage, and the output voltage this supplies to the motor is equal to the voltage fed to its base terminal less a voltage drop of about 1.5 volts through the device. However, output currents of a few amps can be supplied even if the input signal can supply only a milliamp or two.

With IC1 set with input '0' selected, no signal is applied to this input terminal, and R1 therefore cuts off Tr1 and prevents any power being supplied to the motor. This provides the "off" setting. With input '7' selected, the base of Tr1 is connected direct to the positive supply rail, and virtually the full positive supply voltage is fed to the motor. There is actually some voltage drop introduced by IC1 due to the resistance through switch '7', but this is very small and will add little to the normal voltage drop through Tr1.

With any other switch selected there is one of the preset resistors (VR1 to VR6) switched into circuit so as to form a potential divider in conjunction with R1. This gives a series of six switched voltages, and the preset resistors are adjusted to give a series of motor speeds that progress from very slow with VR1 selected through to almost maximum speed with VR6 selected. It would be possible to use a series of fixed value resistors in place of the preset types, but this might not work well in practice as different electric motors respond to changes in supply voltage in different ways. Some will still operate quite powerfully at half their rated maximum voltage, whereas other types will barely operate at all. Having the voltages preset enables the range of voltages to be trimmed to precisely match both the characteristics of the motor, and your exact requirements.

As it stands the circuit will operate perfectly well with supply

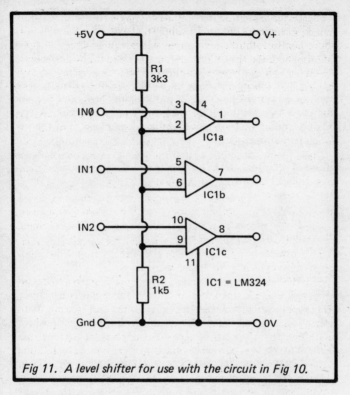

Fig 11. A level shifter for use with the circuit in Fig 10.

voltages of about 5 or 6 volts, but with higher voltages the output
levels from the controlling device will be inadequate to drive the
digital inputs of IC1 properly. This problem is easily overcome by
driving each input via the simple interface circuit shown in Figure
11. If we consider IC1a first, this is just an operational amplifier
comparator with R1 and R2 providing the reference voltage to the
inverting input. This voltage is just under 1.5 volts, and is
therefore between valid·logic 0 and logic 1 levels. If the input
voltage is at logic 0 the output of IC1a therefore goes low (little
more than 0 volts), but if it is at logic 1 the output goes high (to
about 1 volt less than V+). Note that IC1 must be powered from
the same supply as the speed control circuit and not from the 5 volt
output of the computer, so that it provides the required step up in
voltage and drives the 4051BE device properly.

Three of these circuits are needed in order to interface three digital outputs to the control inputs of the 4051BE integrated circuit, but as the LM324 is a quad operational amplifier it can provide all three operational amplifiers. R1 and R2 provide the reference voltage for all three comparators.

One final but important point to note about this controller is that the power dissipated in Tr1 can be quite high, and it should therefore be mounted on a reasonably large heatsink. A type having a rating of 2.6 degrees Centigrade per watt or less should be more than adequate.

Components for Speed Controller (Fig. 10)
Resistors, all ¼ watt 5% carbon film
R1	4k7
R2	4k7

Potentiometers
VR1 to VR6	47k hor. preset (6 off)

Semiconductors
IC1	4051BE
Tr1	TIP122
D1	1N4148

Miscellaneous
Circuit board, large heatsink, 16 pin DIL IC holder, wire, etc.

Addition Components for 5V Logic Interface (Fig. 11).
Resistors, all ¼ watt 5% carbon film
R1	3k3
R2	1k5

Semiconductor
IC1	LM324

Pulse Control
Speed controllers of the type just described are known as constant voltage controllers, as they are effectively providing a stabilised voltage to the motor. This gives a reasonable level of performance, but at low and medium speeds the speed regulation of the

motor is not all that it could be. The problem is simply that a increase in the mechanical loading on the motor results in a large increase in the supply current that is drawn by the motor in an attempt to meet the demand for increased power. Provided the power supply is up to the task, to a large extent the increase in power will be met, but it will not be met in full, and any lack in the regulation efficiency of the controller will result in a drop in the supply voltage and a consequent large shortfall in the power supplied to the motor. With a decrease in mechanical loading on the motor the opposite occurs, with a large decrease in the current consumption. This gives a reduction in the power fed to the motor, but not enough to give good speed regulation, especially if the controller has poor regulation and the output voltage increases with the reduced loading.

The practical result of this is that with reduced loading the motor can tend to run much faster than required. Probably of greater importance, with increased mechanical loading it can tend to run very slowly, and there is a strong risk of it stalling and ceasing to operate at all. A high degree of regulation efficieny from the controller can minimise this effect, but will not eliminate it altogether. One method of obtaining improved speed regulation is to, use the so called over-compensated regulator type. As its name suggests, with this type of controller the regulator circuit over-compensates for any changes in electrical loading. For example, with increased loading the output voltage increases, forcing more current through the motor and providing it with a substantially increased power level. This can give excellent speed regulation with stalling becoming practically impossible, but ideally the controller should have characteristics which are carefully matched to those of the electric motor. Otherwise there is a risk of what could be termed over-over-compensation, with the motor actually speeding up under increased mechanical loading, and slowing up with decreased loading.

Pulsed control is probably the best method of control in cases where good results with a wide range of electric motors is required. With this type of controller the signal fed to the motor is not a straightforward DC type, but is a pulsed signal. Figure 12 helps to explain the way in which this system of speed control operates.

At maximum power the waveform of Figure 12(a) is supplied to the motor. Although this is a pulsed waveform, the output is fully

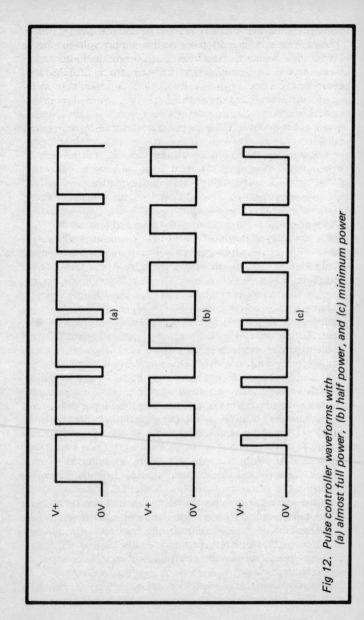

Fig 12. Pulse controller waveforms with
(a) almost full power, (b) half power, and (c) minimum power

positive for the vast majority of the time and the average output voltage is only marginally less than the supply voltage. Figure 12(b) shows the output waveform at half power, and with a 1 to 1 mark-space ratio the output is fully positive for 50% of the time, giving an average output voltage equal to half the supply potential. Figure 12(c) shows the output waveform at minimum power, and here there are only very brief positive pulses giving an average output potential that is only a fraction of the supply voltage.

Although small DC electric motors are not designed for use with a pulsed DC supply, provided the signal is not at a very high or a very low frequency they will operate perfectly well from this type of power source. In fact it has the advantage of giving excellent speed regulation, and this comes about due to the fact that the motor is driven at full power during each output pulse. Thus, when operating at low and medium speeds the motor is kept under firm control, and in particular the normal tendency for it to stall under heavy loading is strongly resisted by the pulses at full power.

Pulser Circuit

Figure 13 shows the circuit diagram of a simple but effective pulse controller for three bit binary control. In fact Figure 13 is the voltage to pulse converter, and it must be used in conjunction with the simple digital to analogue converter circuit of Figure 14.

Taking the operation of Figure 13 first, the circuit is basically just the well known operational amplifier astable (oscillator) circuit. For the moment we will assume that the input voltage is at the normal (for this type of oscillator) half the supply potential bias level. Initially C1 is uncharged, and the bias voltage fed to R1 therefore takes the output of IC1 high, C1 then charges via R3 until the charge voltage exceeds the voltage at the non-inverting input of IC1. This voltage is not half the supply potential since R2 (which connects to the output of IC1 which is in the high state) pulls this voltage higher. In fact it takes the bias voltage to about 75% of the supply potential. When this charge level is reached, the output of IC1 goes to the low state.

R2 now has the effect of taking the bias level at IC1's non-inverting input lower instead of higher, making it only about 25% of the supply voltage. C1 now discharges through R3 and IC1's output stage until this bias level is reached, whereupon the output of IC1 triggers to the high state again and C1 starts to charge up

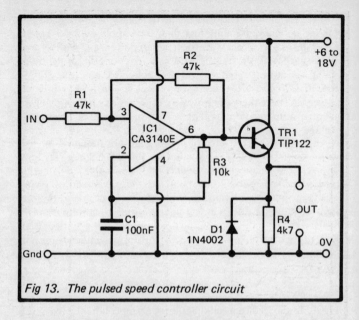

Fig 13. The pulsed speed controller circuit

again. This takes things back to the beginning again, and the circuit continues to oscillate in this manner, generating a squarewave signal with a 1 to 1 mark space ratio at the output of IC1. This signal is buffered by Tr1 and used to drive the motor.

The important factor here is that the 1 to 1 mark-space ratio gives an average output voltage which is equal to half the supply voltage, which is the same as the input voltage fed to R1. If the input voltage is reduced, then the average output voltage is also reduced. If the input voltage is increased, then the average output voltage is increased by the same amount. At first sight this may seem to be impossible, since it would require the charge and discharge rates of C1 to be different, but the charge and discharge resistance is governed by the value of R3 which is the same for both parts of the cycle. However, the charge rate is also governed by the voltage across R3, and it is this that changes, and becomes unequal on each half cycle.

To demonstrate this point, assume that the input voltage is little more than zero volts. C1 then has to charge until the voltage across it reaches about half the supply voltage (since R1 and R2 are virtually connected across the supply rails). The potential at

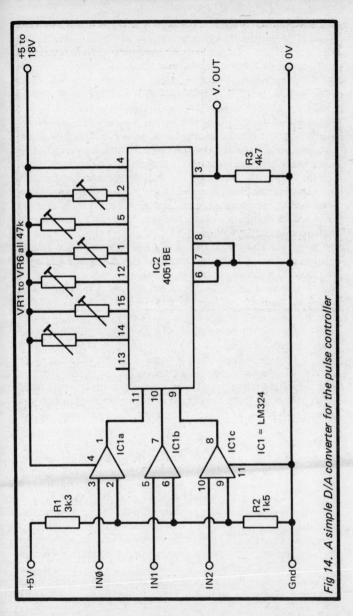

Fig 14. A simple D/A converter for the pulse controller

31

which the circuit reverts to the charge cycle is practically zero volts (since R1 an R2 are then both practically wired to the 0 volt rail). The time taken for C1 to charge to the upper threshold voltage is quite short, with the voltage across R3 varying from practically the full supply voltage to around half the supply potential. This ensures that there is always sufficient voltage across R3 to produce a strong current flow and rapid charging of C1. The situation is different during the discharge cycle when the voltage across R3 starts at half the supply voltage, but steadily dwindles to virtually nothing before the threshold voltage is reached. This gives a very long discharge time in comparison to the charge time, and the output of IC1 is in the low state for much longer than it is in the high state. Thus the required low average output voltage is obtained. Using a high input voltage has the opposite effect, and gives a slow charge rate plus a fast discharge rate, which gives a high average output voltage.

One slight flaw with this arrangement is that the output frequency changes quite considerably with changes in the input voltage, and it increases as the input voltage is raised. This is not a major problem though, as by carefully choosing the component values the output frequency can be kept within acceptable limits over the full input voltage range. Another minor snag is that at input voltages just below the full supply potential the circuit ceases to oscillate. This is due to the output stage of IC1 not being able to provide voltages within about one volt of the positive supply rail. This does not really matter since the circuit hangs up with the output fully positive, and this could actually be regarded as an advantage since it means that full power is genuinely full power, with no power being lost during brief negative output half cycles.

Another consequence of IC1 not being able to provide an output voltage equal to the full positive supply potential is that the maximum output voltage is reduced by about one volt or so in addition to the 15 volts or thereabouts which is dropped through Tr1. The supply voltage should therefore be about three volts or so more than the required maximum output voltage to the motor. The switching nature of the output signal ensures that there is never a large amount of power dissipated in Tr1, but with output currents of more than just a few hundred milliamps it will still require a small heatsink.

Turning now to the circuit diagram of the digital to analogue converter Figure 14, this has obvious similarities to Figures

10 and 11 which were discussed earlier. In actual fact the input side of the circuit is the triple level shifter circuit of Figure 11. This drives the analogue to digital converter circuit which is exactly the same as the relevant section of Figure 10. As the circuit is really just a revamp of two circuits that were described earlier, we will not consider them in any more detail here.

Components for Pulse Speed Controller (Fig. 13).
Resistors, all ¼ watt 5% carbon film

R1	47k
R2	47k
R3	10k
R4	4k7

Capacitor
C1	100nF polyester

Semiconductors
IC1	CA3140E
Tr1	TIP122
D1	1N4002

Miscellaneous
Circuit board, small heatsink, wire, etc.

Additional Components For D/A Converter (Fig. 14).
Resistors, all ¼ watt 5% carbon film

R1	3k3
R2	1k5
R3	4k7

Potentiometers
VR1 to VR6	All 47k hor. preset (6 off)

Semiconductors
IC1	LM324
IC2	4051BE

Fast Stop
Precise control using ordinary DC electric motors is hampered by their reluctance to stop when the power is switched off. On testing

a 12 volt DC motor it was found to take some 1.5 seconds or thereabouts to stop when the power was switched off, and although this was admittedly under zero load conditions, it does show the large amount of overshoot that can occur. It would be possible to devise some form of mechanical breaking controlled from the computer via a solenoid, but for most purposes a simple system of automatic electronic breaking, or a "fast stop" circuit as they are often called, is all that is required.

Circuits of this type operate by placing a short circuit across the electric motor when it is switched off. This is something that can be achieved very easily with relay control, and it is merely necessary to use a changeover contact to switch the non-earthy side of the motor between the positive and 0 volt supply rails. The alternative of using separate normally open and normally closed contacts to provide the switching is not recommended as there would be a danger of both contacts being closed momentarily, producing a short circuit across the supply lines. This could actually occur using a set of changeover contacts if they were of the make before break variety rather than the break before make type. However, on checking an assortment of relays none seemed to be of the make before break type, and a set of changeover contacts seems to represent a perfectly safe way of doing things.

On the face of it there is no advantage in placing a short circuit across the motor when it is switched off, but this can be quite effective as the free-wheeling electric motor operates in reverse as a simple electric generator. By placing a short circuit across the motor the signal generated by the motor is effectively fed back into it and used to drive it. The salient point here is that the voltage generated by the motor has a polarity that results in it opposing the rotation of the motor. This can produce a substantial reduction in the time taken for the motor to cruise to a halt, and on testing the 12 volt motor referred to earlier with a fast stop circuit, the time taken for it to come to a halt was reduced from about 1.5 seconds to under half a second, representing a reduction of around 75%.

It is possible to have an electronic fast stop circuit which does not use any relay contacts, but as with the relay type, care has to be exercised in order to avoid short circuits on the supply lines. This is, if anything, more important with a semiconductor switching circuit, since any brief short circuits could instantly destroy the two devices concerned. With a relay circuit the only consequence might be some reduction in the contact life.

34

Figure 15 shows a safe but effective relayless fast stop circuit. This is actually the same as the motor controller circuit of Figure 9 which was discussed earlier in this chapter, apart that is, from the inclusion of Tr3. With this device included, the output stage of the circuit becomes a complementary emitter follower type, similar to those used in audio power amplifiers. With the motor switched on, Tr2 drives the motor and Tr3 becomes cut off so that it plays no active role in the circuit. When the motor is switched off it is Tr2 that becomes cut off and Tr3 that is biased hard into conduction, virtually short circuiting the electric motor. This arrangement is completely safe as during the transition from one state to the other, at no stage do both devices become simultaneously biased into conduction. In fact during the switch over there is a brief period when both transistors become switched off.

There is no need for Tr3 to be a high power device or to be fitted with a heatsink, as it will normally only be handling relatively low power levels for brief and infrequent periods of time. Even with rapid and continuous switching of the motor it is unlikely that Tr3 would become noticeably warm.

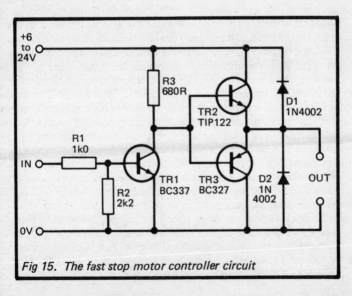

Fig 15. The fast stop motor controller circuit

Components for Fast Stop Circuit (Fig. 15)
Resistors, all ¼ watt 5% carbon film except where noted.

R1	1k
R2	2k2
R3	680R 1W

Semiconductors

Tr1	BC337
Tr2	TIP122
Tr3	BC327
D1	1N4002
D2	1N4002

Miscellaneous
Circuit board, small heatsink, wire, etc.

Stepper Motors
Ordinary DC electric motors are the most popular type for low cost robotics applications due to their wide availability, low cost, and the relative ease with which they can be controlled. They have only one serious rival, and this is the so called "stepper" type motor. As its name suggests, rather than providing continuous rotation when it is activated, a stepper motor moves in small steps of typically just a few degrees per step. With an ordinary electric motor when driving something like a robot arm or a clasper there is normally a enormous step-down ratio from the motor to the moving parts, and this gives quite precise control. It also gives a considerable amount of force if it is needed. With a stepper motor quite a high degree of precision is obtained at the drive shaft, and in most applications it is possible to use a low reduction gear ratio, or even to just have a simple direct drive mechanism. An important point to bear in mind when using stepper motors is that they generally provide less power than an ordinary electric motor of comparable size. Another important factor to keep in mind is that they are relatively expensive, less readily available, and require more complex and expensive driver circuits.

Stepper motors are quite simple in principle, and Figure 16 helps to explain the basic way in which they function in what is admittedly a rather over simplified fashion. Four electromagnets surround a rotor which contains a bar magnet. Like poles of a magnet repel one another, unlike poles attract each other, and

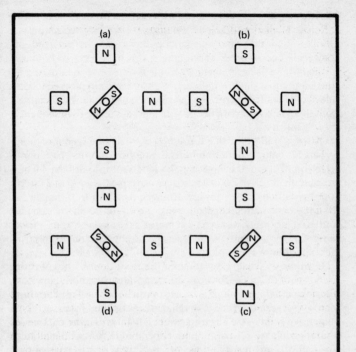

Fig 16. A stepper motor effectively provides a rotating magnetic field which the magnetised rotor follows

with the electromagnets set to have the magnetic polarities of Figure 16(a), the rotator is drawn into the position shown. By changing the polarities of the electromagnets to those shown in Figure 16(b) the rotor is pulled through 90 degrees, and by further changing the polarities as indicated in Figures 16(c) and 16(d) it can be stepped through two further 90 degree steps. Then going back to the original set of polarities steps the motor through another 90 degrees and completes a full 360 degree turn.

By continuously switching the electromagnets in the correct manner the rotor can be made to rotate continuously, and it can be stopped at whichever of the four positions is required. By reversing the switching sequence it can be stepped in the opposite direction. As a north pole is always opposite a south pole, the four electromagnets can be replaced with two electromagnets in a sort of cross formation. Each electromagnet then has two antiphase windings so that the magnetic polarity can be selected by powering one or other of windings. This may seem to be more difficult than using changeover contacts to reverse the polarity of the supply to a single winding, but as we have already seen, with electronic control a true changeover action provides difficulties. Simply switching on two out of four windings in the right sequence is very much easier.

A stepper motor with a resolution of 90 degrees is not of great practical value, but commercial stepper motors use more electromagnets and magnetic poles in the rotor to achieve higher resolution. Steps of 7.5 or 15 degrees are typical (i.e. 48 or 24 steps per revolution). The coils are arranged in sets of four though, so that the basic method of sequencing the motor is still the same as outlined above. This type of motor is called a "four phase unipolar" motor, and it is the type which is most frequently used in simple robotics applications.

Obviously a computer could easily be made to control a stepper motor with the aid of four driver circuits and software to provide the correct sequencing. It is easier to use a special stepper motor driver integrated circuit though, and although this is a more expensive solution, it has a couple of advantages. One of these is that it enables fewer output lines to be used to control the motor. Instead of four, just two lines are required, one to control the direction of the motor and the other to provide clock pulses to step the motor through the required number of settings. Often stepper motor driver circuits have other facilities, such as a reset input which can be used to set the outputs of the driver to their start states. However, it is not essential to use any additional inputs such as these, and basic control of the motor can be achieved with only two output lines.

Stepper Circuit

There are several integrated circuits which can be used for stepper motor control, but the SAA1027 is probably the best choice. This is not so much because it offers exceptional performance and an unrivalled range of features, as the fact that it is relatively easy to obtain and the cost is quite reasonable. It provides a more than adequate level of performance. Figure 17 shows the circuit diagram of a simple stepper motor controller based on the SAA1027.

38

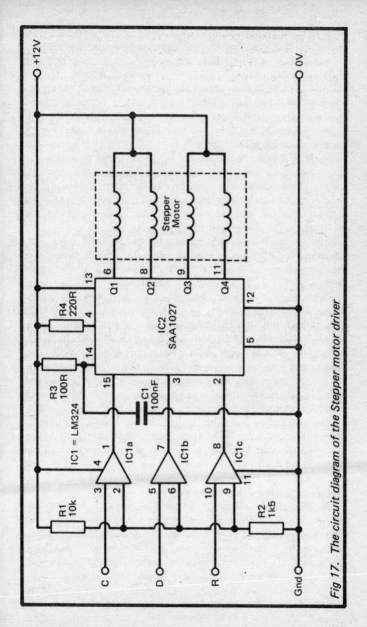

Fig 17. The circuit diagram of the Stepper motor driver

39

With the SAA1027 doing most of the work without the need for many discrete components the circuit is remarkably straightforward. The SAA1027 has four open collector outputs which directly drive the coils of the stepper motor, and note that the "common" terminal (or terminals) of the motor must connect to the positive supply rail and not the 0 volt rail. Note also that no discrete protection diodes are needed across the coils of the motor as the SAA1027 has a built-in protection diode between each output and the positive supply rail.

There are three inputs to the SAA1027, and these are the direction, reset, and clock pulse inputs. The circuit is powered from a 12 volt supply, and it requires 12 volt control signals rather than normal 5 volt logic types. The three operational amplifiers of IC1 are therefore used to give the necessary level shifting. The "C" input is the clock input, and the pulses to step the motor are supplied to this input. The outputs of IC2 change state on a high to low transition of the clock input incidentally, and as the circuit is edge triggered the length of the input pulses is not of great importance. The data sheet does not indicate the minimum acceptable pulse duration, but pulses as short as a few microseconds seem to be perfectly suitable (the switching speed of IC1a is probably the limiting factor in this case). Note that the maximum usable clock frequency is determined by the characteristics of the electric motor and not by the driver circuit. With most motors the maximum acceptable frequency will be only a few Hertz, and this is something which can be determined by trial and error if necessary. It will be apparent from this that stepper motors are not normally capable of speeds of around a few thousand RPM like ordinary DC types, and may in fact only be able to do a few dozen RPM when running flat out. Their purpose is to give precision movement and not high speed, and in order to fully exploit their precision it is important not to provide clock pulses faster than they can be processed as this would get the computer and the motor out of step.

The "D" input controls the direction of the motor, and with the motor connected correctly it provides rotation in a clockwise direction when this input is low, and anticlockwise rotation when it is high. "R" is the reset input, and this sets the four outputs back to their initial states if it is pulsed low. In most cases this input will not be required, and it can simply be tied to the positive supply rail.

The following table indicates the logic state of each output terminal at each of the four output phases, and for both direction input settings.

Clock Cycle	"D"=LOW				"D"=HIGH			
	Q1	Q2	Q3	Q4	Q1	Q2	Q3	Q4
0	L	H	L	H	L	H	L	H
1	H	L	L	H	L	H	H	L
2	H	L	H	L	H	L	H	L
3	L	H	H	L	H	L	L	H

This is not just of academic interest, and this table is useful for checking purposes if the system fails to operate properly. If the SAA1027 is providing the right sequences of output states but the motor does not function properly, either the motor is faulty or it is not connected properly. Finding the right method of connection might be a little awkward if the retailer who supplies the motor can not provide the necessary information, but in most cases the motor will be supplied with a leaflet that gives full connection details or the necessary information will be found in the retailer's catalogue. The stepper motors that I have used have all had flying leads which are colour coded as in one or other of the two tables shown below:-

Colour	Terminal	Colour	Terminal
GREEN	COMMON	WHITE	COMMON
GREEN	COMMON	WHITE	COMMON
BLUE	INPUT 1	BROWN	INPUT 1
YELLOW	INPUT 2	ORANGE	INPUT 2
RED	INPUT 3	RED	INPUT 3
WHITE	INPUT 4	BLACK	INPUT 4

If necessary trial and error can be used to find the correct method of connection, and although this might be quite time consuming, there is little risk of damaging the motor by connecting it incorrectly. It will be seen from the above tables that there are normally two "common" terminals, one for each pair of windings. These are both connected to the positive supply when the motor is driven from an SAA1027.

A few points have to be borne in mind when using this interface, and one of these is that power is always applied to two of the windings in the motor whether it is being stepped or not. This is one respect in which a stepper motor differs from an ordinary DC motor, which always operates when power is applied to it. With a stepper motor it is not simply applying power to a couple of its windings that cause it to operate, but switching power between windings in the appropriate manner. It is perfectly acceptable to leave the motor with two of its windings being continuously fed with power, and neither the motor or the driver device should overheat. If the equipment is mains powered there is little point in doing anything else, but if the system is battery powered it is obviously possible to make a worthwhile power saving by deactivating the supply to the common terminals of the motor during periods when the latter will be inoperative. This can be accomplished using one of the motor control circuits featured earlier in this chapter.

Although the circuit of Figure 17 is shown as operating with a 12 volt supply, the SAA1027 will in fact work properly over a 9.5 to 18 volt supply range. However, most of the stepper motors that are available from electronic component retailers seem to have 12 volt coils. The absolute maximum output current rating of the SAA1027 is 500 milliamps (0.5 amps), which with a 12 volt supply corresponds to a coil resistance of 24 ohms. This accordingly represents the lowest coil resistance that can be used with the circuit (most stepper motors seem to have a coil resistance in the region of 100 ohms, and the circuit is capable of driving most types).

The circuit is easily tested by using a software loop and time delay to send a few pulses per second to the clock input and checking that the motor steps properly. Do not forget to try the direction input at both logic state to ensure that it switches the direction of rotation properly.

Components for Stepper Motor Driver (Fig. 17)
Resistors, ¼ watt 5% carbon film except where noted

R1	10k
R2	1k5
R2	100R
R3	220R 1W

Capacitor

C1	100nF ceramic

Semiconductors

IC1	LM324
IC2	SAA1027

42

Miscellaneous
Circuit board, 4 phase unipolar 12 volt (about 100R per phase)
stepper motor, wire, etc.

Pulsing
It is possible to obtain a sort of pseudo stepper motor action from
an ordinary DC electric motor, but it has to be admitted that such
a system does not give the same degree of accuracy as that
obtained from a real stepper motor. It is not possible to obtain
steps of just a few degrees direct at the drive shaft, but using
suitable reduction gearing steps as small as required can be
achieved. The main drawback with stepping an ordinary motor is
that it does not give completely repeatable results. With a real
stepper motor it can be taken through a few hundred revolutions,
and then reversed back to exactly its original starting position.
There will of course be some degree of error, but this error is due
to things such as any backlash in the mechanics of the system, and
the motor's rotor positions having a limit on their degree of
accuracy. We would normally be talking in terms of very small
errors in both cases though, and stepper motors are used in critical
applications such as plotters for producing technical drawings,
where excellent accuracy and repeatability are obviously of
paramount importance. When stepping an ordinary DC motor
there is usually a tendency for it to drift slightly, as the shaft
positions are not so rigidly defined as with a stepper motor.

Despite this drawback, pulsing of an ordinary motor to give a
pseudo stepper motor action is a useful technique which offers a
low cost alternative to real stepper motors. The slight lack of
accuracy is not necessarily of prime importance, and can be of no
significance in applications where a sensor or sensors are being
used to help control things. In fact a system of pulsing generally
works very well indeed when applied to a system which is
primarily under the control of sensors of some kind. The general
arrangement in these cases is to step the motor, read information
from the sensors to determine what must be done next, step the
motor again if necessary, read information from the sensors
again, and so on. This may seem to be a slow way of doing things,
but with a computer controlling things a system of this type can
operate at a perfectly respectable speed. Provided the steps are
made small enough it keeps the system under quite rigid control.
With systems that use DC motors running normally there is a risk

of considerable overshoot due to the time taken for sensors, the controlling circuit, and the motors to respond to changes. Thus the increased operating speed may be at the expense of accuracy and reliability. The main danger is when severe overshoot causes it to either hang-up or run out of control.

Pulser Circuit

Nothing very elaborate is needed in order to pulse a DC motor, and it can be achieved using a circuit of the type shown in Figure 9 (and described previously), with software generated pulses of the appropriate duration driving the circuit. Or better still, the fast stop controller of Figure 15 could be used in this way. It is generally easier to drive the motor via a simple pulse generator circuit though. The computer still has to provide output pulses on the output line in order to give the stepping action, but by driving the motor via a pulse generator circuit the duration of the output pulses from the computer is rendered irrelevant. This greatly simplifies the software since it is then just a matter of setting the output line high and then immediately setting it low again in order to step the motor. This can easily be done from BASIC or when using machine code programs, and the only pitfall that has to be avoided is to ensure that sufficient time is left between generating a pulse and reading a sensor or sending the next pulse. This is easily achieved by adding delay loops into the program, and if necessary the optimum delay time can simply be determined using trial and error.

The circuit diagram of a simple motor pulser is given in Figure 18. This is basically just a monostable multivibrator driving the motor via a high current output stage. The choice of monostable is an important one, and it is essential for it to be a non-retriggerable type. In other words, it must be triggered by the input going from the low state to the high state, with the length of time that the input stays high having no effect whatever on the output pulse duration. Some types of monostable multivibrator will only operate as pulse lengtheners, and if the input pulse is longer than the required output pulse, the actual output pulse duration tends to be equal to the input pulse length, or in some cases this length plus the required output pulse time. In most instances, even using software written in a relatively slow computer language such as BASIC, it would probably be possible to produce output pulses of short enough duration for correct operation with a retriggerable monostable, but by using a non-

44

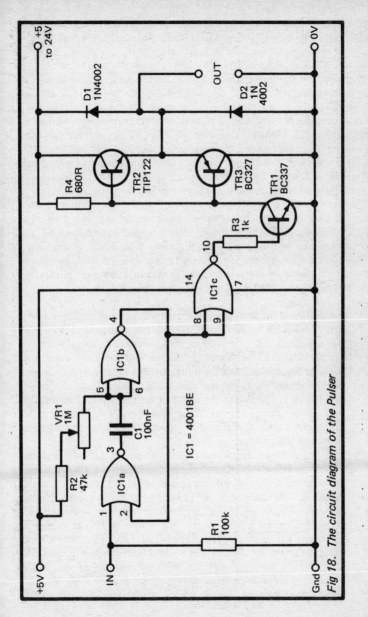

Fig 18. The circuit diagram of the Pulser

45

retriggerable type things are that much easier, and the software can be written in a form which is convenient to the writer, rather than having to rigidly stick to a routine that suits the interface.

IC1 acts as the monostable, and this is a CMOS 4001BE quad 2 input NOR gate connected in a conventional circuit configuration. In fact it is IC1a and IC1b that form the monostable, and IC1c is merely an inverter at the output of the circuit. This converts the positive output pulses from IC1b into negative pulses to suit the following circuitry. This type of monostable provides the required positive edge triggering and is a non- retriggerable circuit. VR1 enables the output pulse duration to be varied from about 32ms at minimum resistance to about 712ms at maximum resistance. This range should be sufficient for most requirements, but it varies in proportion to the value of timing capacitor C1, and it can therefore be changed by altering the value of this component. R1 simply ties the input of the circuit to ground if it should be disconnected from the controlling device at any time, and this protects the input against static damage. The two inputs of the unused gate are connected to the positive supply rail for the same reason, but this gate is otherwise ignored.

The output stage may have a familiar look to it, and it is basically just the fast stop motor controller circuit of Figure 15. It differs from this only in that the resistor from the base of Tr1 to the 0 volt supply rail has been omitted. Since the drive signal is always obtained from a CMOS circuit, and a CMOS output when low is within a few millivolts of the 0 volt supply rail, there is no danger of Tr1 being held in the "on" state, and this resistor is unnecessary. The fast stop version of the controller is preferable as it gives more precise and repeatable results, but it has to be emphasized that results will not equal those obtained using a proper stepper motor.

Adjustment of the circuit should not prove difficult, and the optimum setting for VR1 will depend on the way in which the unit is to be used. To aid adjustment it is helpful to run a simple program in the computer that pulses the motor at approximately one second intervals, or perhaps the program could be designed to provide an output pulse each time a key of the keyboard is operated. VR1 can be adjusted to give a fraction of a turn on each pulse, or a number of turns, as required. If you rotate the shaft of an electric motor by hand you will find that it does not freely rotate, but tends to jump to certain positions (probably three of these per rotation). These represent the minimum practical movement per pulse, and for optimum precision VR1 should be adjusted to give this 120 degrees of rotation per pulse. In some applications this might be too small, making the system impractically slow in operation, and VR1 should then be adjusted for a greater amount of rotation on each pulse. However, do not use very long pulses or the advantages of pulsing are likely to be lost.

Components for Pulser (Fig. 18)
Resistors, all ¼ watt 5% carbon film except where noted.

R1	100k
R2	47k
R3	1k
R4	680R 1W

Potentiometer

VR1	1M linear

Capacitor

C1	100nF polyester

Semiconductors

IC1	4001BE
Tr1	BC337
Tr2	TIP122
Tr3	BC327
D1	1N4002
D2	1N4002

Miscellaneous
Circuit board, 14 pin DIL IC holder, small heatsink, etc.

Power Supplies
The best power source for a robot depends very much its type, and while a mains power supply is a good choice in many applications with its negligible running costs, it is obviously not applicable where a self contained unit is required. In the vast majority of cases a mains power supply is perfectly suitable, as many robots are of the arm variety and therefore immobile, and most others are not self contained but are instead controlled via a cable from a home computer or other controlling device. With this so called umbilical method of control, the lead running from the controller

to the robot may as well carry power as well as control signals.

Power supplies is a complete subject in itself, and it is not possible to give details of a full range of power supply circuits here. Further information on this subject can be found in Books No. BP76 *Power Supply Projects* and No. BP192, *More Advanced Power Supply Projects* from the same publisher and author as this publication. However, for most purposes the power supply circuit of Figure 19 will suffice.

The mains supply is taken to the primary of mains transformer T1 by way of on/off switch S1. The mains transformer provides safety isolation as well as a voltage step-down. D1 and D2 provide full wave (push-pull) rectification of T1's output and C1 provides substantial smoothing of the output.

An unloaded voltage of around 24 volts is present across C1, and this falls considerably under full load. In order to give good performance in most robotics applications it is necessary to have a well regulated supply, and a supply voltage in the range 6 to 12 volts is the normal requirement. IC1 provides the necessary

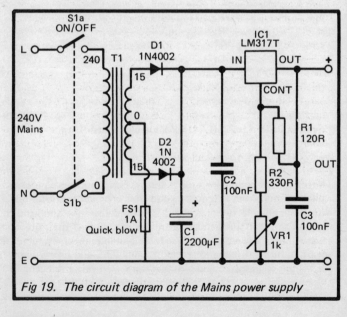

Fig 19. The circuit diagram of the Mains power supply

regulation, and this is a three terminal adjustable voltage regulator. The basic action provided by IC1 is to stabilise the current through R1 at a level that gives a nominal 1.25 volts across this component, but in effect the current through the R2 and VR1 is controlled as well. Thus the voltage across this series of three resistors is stabilised, and so is the output voltage since the resistor chain is connected across the output of the supply. By adjusting the value of VR1 the output voltage can be varied from just under 5 volts at minimum resistance to around 15 volts with VR1 at maximum value. With output voltages of more than 12 volts there may be a significant fall in the output potential under heavy loading, but if good performance at high output voltages is important this problem can be largely alleviated by using a transformer having a 2 amp rating in the T1 position.

The circuit can provide continuous output currents of up to 1 amp. IC1 provides current limiting that prevents the output current from exceeding about 2 amps, and this should protect both the supply and the powered equipment against any short term overloads or short circuits. In the event of prolonged overloading FS1 will "blow" and protect the circuit.

When constructing any piece of equipment which connects to the mains it is absolutely essential to rigidly observe the standard safety precautions. The unit must be housed in a case which has a screw fitting lid or cover and not a clip-on type (which would give easy access to the dangerous mains wiring). Any exposed metal work, including things such as fixing screws, should be earthed to the mains earth lead. This is most easily accomplished by using a case of all metal construction and then earthing this to the mains earth lead. Anything metal which is fixed to the case will then automatically be earthed. It is a good idea to insulate any exposed mains wiring so that when the case is opened there is still no easy way of coming into contact with a "live" lead.

In order for decoupling capacitors C2 and C3 to have optimum effectiveness at aiding good stability they should be mounted physically close to IC1. The latter will need a sizeable heatsink if overheating is to be avoided, especially if the supply is used to provide low voltages at high output currents. If the supply unit has a metal case it will probably be possible to mount IC1 on this and use it as the heatsink. Alternatively, one of the larger ready-made heatsinks is suitable, and a type having a rating of 2.6 degrees Centigrade per watt or less should suffice. Note that the heat-tab of the LM317T connects internally to its output terminal, and that

49

in most cases it will therefore be necessary to insulate it from the heatsink using the standard ("plastic power" type) insulation set.

Components for Power Supply (Fig. 19)
Resistors, all 0.4 or 0.6W 1% metal film
R1	120R
R2	330R

Potentiometer
VR1	1k linear

Capacitors
C1	2200μF 25V elect
C2	100nF ceramic
C3	100nF ceramic

Semiconductors
IC1	LM317T
D1	1N4002
D2	1N4002

Miscellaneous
S1	Rotary mains switch
FS1	1 amp 20mm quick-blow
T1	Mains primary, 15-0-15V 1 amp or 2 amp secondary

Case, circuit board, 20mm fuseholder, wire, etc.

Batteries
Battery operation of small DC motors is a practical proposition, but the current consumptions tend to be quite high which makes the battery life somewhat limited even if the more expensive types, specifically intended for high power applications are used. Rechargeable nickel-cadmium batteries are probably the best choice as although they are relatively expensive initially and there is the additional cost of the charger to take into account, they can be recharged hundreds of times and will last many years. This makes them relatively cheap in the medium and long terms. Another advantage of nickel-cadmium cells is their very low internal resistance which gives good voltage regulation with only a small voltage drop even at very high load currents.

One slight drawback of the low internal resistance is that it can result in very high currents flowing in the event of short circuits or other serious overloads. This has the potential to cause a lot of expensive damage to the circuit being powered by the batteries. A fuse in series with the batteries provides some protection, but it may not be fast enough in operation to prevent damage in many cases. It is probably worthwhile including some form of electronic current limiting between the batteries and the powered equipment, and a suitable circuit appears in Figure 20.

The circuit is basically the same as the standard current limiting type that is incorporated in many power supply designs that are based on discrete components, and is actually the basis for the current limiting circuit in several integrated circuit voltage regulators as well. It is a well tried and tested design which operates very rapidly and is very reliable in use. Tr2 operates as an emitter follower stage which is normally biased into conduction by R1, and the input supply is able to flow straight through to the output via Tr2 and R2. Obviously there is some voltage loss across these, and this amounts to a total of around 1.5 to 2 volts, depending on the amount of supply current involved. One or two

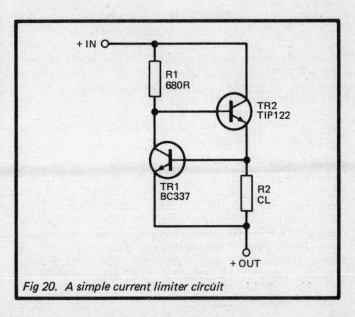

Fig 20. A simple current limiter circuit

51

extra batteries must therefore be used in order to boost the input voltage slightly to compensate for the losses through the circuit.

At low output currents the voltage developed across R2 is too low to switch on Tr1, which consequently has no effect on the circuit. If the current flow is large enough to produce about 0.6 volts or so across R2, then Tr1 is brought into conduction, and it tends to tap off some of Tr2's base current through the load and to earth. This has the effect of pulling the output voltage lower, and the more heavily the output is loaded above this point, the more negative the output is taken. This prevents any significant increase in the output current, and even with a short circuit across the output the current flow will be that which is just sufficient to give about 0.65 volts across R2.

The circuit therefore gives the required current limiting, and the short circuit current is controlled by the value of R2. The value needed in the R2 position is equal to 0.65 divided by the required maximum output current in amps. This gives the value of R2 in ohms. As a simple example, for a maximum output current of 500 milliamps (0.5 amps) the value for R2 would be 1.3 ohms (0.65 divided by 0.5=1.3). The calculated value will not always be a preferred value in either the E12 or the E24 ranges of values, but it will normally be acceptable to simply select the preferred value which is closest to the calculated figure. If required, greater accuracy can be attained by using two or more resistors in series or in parallel to make up the calculated value. Due to the low value that will normally be required it is not really feasable to use a preset potentiometer to enable the short circuit output current to be precisely trimmed to the correct figure.

Although this circuit may look a little strange in that is connects into the positive supply rail and has no connection to the 0 volt supply rail, this is perfectly correct.

Serial Control

Running a number of control lines from a computer to a robot is not usually a major problem, but it can cause difficulties. This is particularly the case when a small mobile robot is being controlled, as there is a real danger of the stiffness and weight of the cable preventing the unit from moving around properly. Also, with just a thin control cable having a few wires there is little risk of the cable becoming twisted to the point where things get into a hopeless tangle and proceedings have to be brought to a halt, but this is a distinct possibility if the connections are carried by one or two multiway ribbon cables.

The number of wires between the controller and the robot can be reduced by using serial interfacing instead of the parallel variety. With a serial interface all the signals are carried on a single wire (plus the earth wire), but this obviously makes it impossible to send all the signals at once. They must therefore be sent one at a time, in a predetermined sequence, and then decoded back into parallel form at the receiving end of the system. Apart from reducing the number of wires running between the computer and the robot, another advantage of this system is that it enables a robot to be controlled by a computer which does have an RS232C or RS423 serial port, but which does not have a user port or other form of parallel output port.

With normal asynchronous serial signals (the type used with RS232C and RS423 interfaces) the least significant bit is transmitted first, running through in sequence to the most significant bit. For a system of this type to operate properly it is necessary for other signals to be included along with the data bits, and the most important of these is the start bit. This is merely a signal transmitted at the beginning of a byte of data which indicates that a byte is about to be sent, and that the receiving equipment must sample the state on the signal line at regular intervals thereafter until the state of each bit has been determined. The data signals are followed by one or two stop bits, and the main purpose of these is merely to ensure that there is a reasonable gap between transmitted bytes of data so that confusion and consequent decoding errors are avoided at the decoding equipment. In addition to the stop bits there are sometimes parity bits added at the end of each byte, and these are used as a form of error checking. Things are further complicated by the use of two types of parity (odd and even), but parity

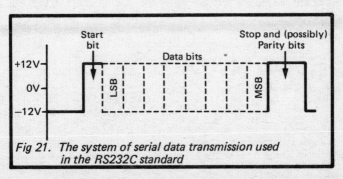

Fig 21.   The system of serial data transmission used
          in the RS232C standard

checking seems to be little used in practice. Figure 21 shows the form which serial signals take, and it should help to explain the way in which the asynchronous serial interface system functions.

In order to correctly decode a serial signal it is important that the decoder should be set up for the right word format (the right number of stop bits, and odd, even, or no parity). There is yet another complication in that with serial systems there is not necessarily the standard eight bits per byte, and five, six, and seven bit word formats are also used (although you are unlikely to encounter five and six bit formats in normal computing). One final complication is that there are a number of baud rates in common use. The baud rate is simply the number of bits transmitted each second with a continuous flow of data, and the standard rates are 50, 75, 110, 150, 300, 600, 1200, 1800, 2400, 4800, 9600, and 19200 baud. With the wrong word format selected it is unlikely that proper decoding would be obtained, and with the wrong baud rate the received data would certainly be completely scrambled.

Decoder Circuit
Decoding serial signals is a quite complex task, but fortunately there are special serial decoder integrated circuits which greatly simplify matters. Some of these are only intended for use with microprocessors, and these are not really suitable for use in a simple stand-alone decoder application. The other type are the UARTs (universal asynchronous receiver transmitters). In common with most other serial interface devices these can both encode parallel data into a serial format, and decode serial signals back into parallel form, but if only decoding is required the transmitter section can just be ignored. They are ideal for our present purposes because they are capable of independent operation with the word format, etc. being programmed by switches or wire links rather than by an on-board microprocessor.

A simple serial decoder circuit is shown in Figure 22, and this is based on the industry standard 6402 UART. RS232C serial signals are not at normal 5 volt logic levels, but at potentials of about plus and minus 12 volts (about half these figures for RS423 signals). These must be processed to take them down to ordinary 0 and 5 volt logic levels before they are applied to IC1. The necessary processing is provided by Tr1 which operates as a simple common emitter switch. This stage provides an inversion as well as the level shifting, but this is correct as IC1 requires an

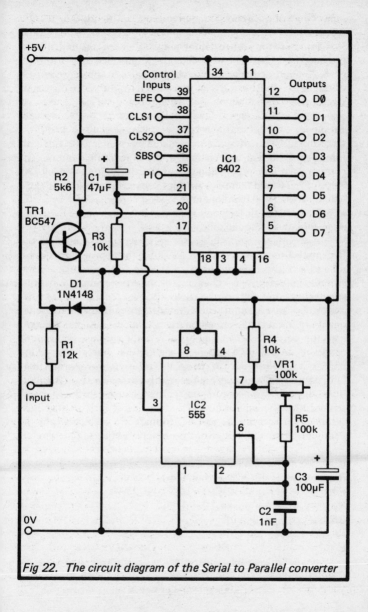

Fig 22. The circuit diagram of the Serial to Parallel converter

55

input signal of the opposite polarity to the raw RS232C or RS423 types.

IC1 requires a positive reset pulse at switch-on, and this is provided by C1 and R3. The baud rate is controlled by an external clock generator circuit, and the clock frequency applied to pin 17 of the device must be sixteen times the required receiving baud rate. In this case a simple 555 astable based on IC2 is used to provide the clock signal, and VR1 is trimmed to give a clock frequency of 4.8kHz which gives a receiving baud rate of 300. Other baud rates can be accommodated by changing the value of timing capacitor C2, and changes in the value of this component give an inversely proportional change in output frequency. A value of 2n2 would therefore permit 150 baud operation, or 470pF would provide 600 baud operation. Most computers can operate at 300 baud though, and this gives a good compromise between operating speed and reliability.

The word format that IC1 is set up to decode is controlled by five inputs (pins 35 to 39) which are tied to the appropriate supply rails to give the required format. These could be controlled by switches to permit easy changing of the word format, but presumably the unit will only be used with one computer in the vast majority of cases, and it will therefore only ever need to decode one word format. The circuit board can then be designed to take each input to the correct supply rail, or link wires can be used to program the inputs. The second method has the advantage of making it relatively easy to change to a different word format at a later date if this should become necessary for some reason (such as if you upgrade to a new computer). Table 1 shows the logic states required on the inputs for each of the word formats that are catered for, and all the normal formats are included (plus a number that are unlikely to be encountered in practice).

Components for Serial Decoder (Fig. 22)
Resistors, all ¼ watt 5% carbon film

R1	12k
R2	5k6
R3	10k
R4	10k
R5	100k

Potentiometer

VR1	100k sub-min preset

Table 1. 6402 Control Words

Pin 35	Pin 36	Pin 37	Pin 38	Pin 39	Data Bits	Parity	Stop Bits
L	L	L	L	L	5	ODD	1
L	H	L	L	L	5	ODD	1.5
L	L	L	L	H	5	EVEN	1
L	H	L	L	H	5	EVEN	1.5
H	L	L	L	X	5	NONE	1
H	H	L	L	X	5	NONE	1.5
L	L	L	H	L	6	ODD	1
L	H	L	H	L	6	ODD	2
L	L	L	H	H	6	EVEN	1
L	H	L	H	H	6	EVEN	2
H	L	L	H	X	6	NONE	1
H	H	L	H	X	6	NONE	2
L	L	H	L	L	7	ODD	1
L	H	H	L	L	7	ODD	2
L	L	H	L	H	7	EVEN	1
L	H	H	L	H	7	EVEN	2
H	L	H	L	X	7	NONE	1
H	H	H	L	X	7	NONE	2
L	L	H	H	L	8	ODD	1
L	H	H	H	L	8	ODD	2
L	L	H	H	H	8	EVEN	1
L	H	H	H	H	8	EVEN	2
H	L	H	H	X	8	NONE	1
H	H	H	H	X	8	NONE	2

X=Either state acceptable

57

Capacitors

C1	47µF 10V elect
C2	1nF polyester
C3	100µF 10V elect

Semiconductors

IC1	6402 UART
IC2	NE555
Tr1	BC547
D1	1N4148

Miscellaneous
Circuit board, 40 pin DIL IC holder, wire, etc.

The outputs of IC1 are latching types, and when a new byte of data is sent to the interface, as soon as decoding has been completed the outputs take up the new set of states and remain in those states until the next byte of data is received. Of course, if a word format having fewer than eight data bits is chosen, not all the outputs will be operative, and it is the most significant bit or bits that become inoperative in these cases. For instance, with seven data bits it is D7 that becomes inoperative. Obviously it is essential to use an eight bit word format if it is important to have all eight output lines available, and most computers support at least one eight bit word format.

RS232C and RS423 interfaces both have provision for handshake lines to control the flow of data between devices. In this case there should be no need to implement any handshaking since the outputs will presumably be controlling motors and solenoids which will immediately respond to new data. Any handshaking will be of a fairly complex type involving sensors on the robot and software in the computer to give the correct responses to information from these.

It is perfectly feasable to use IC1 to transmit information from the sensors back to the computer's serial port, but it might not always be worthwhile doing this. Most robots require a number of control lines to operate the electric motors and solenoids, but in many cases only one or two sensors are present in the design. There is little point in encoding these into serial form if there are a couple of spare digital inputs on the computer that can be used to read them directly. On the other hand, if there are a number of sensors to contend with, or the computer only has a serial port available for interfacing to the robot, then a serial link back to the computer is a practical solution to the problem.

The circuit diagram of Figure 23 shows the necessary modifications to the decoder circuit of Figure 22 to extend it to provide serial transmission. The five control inputs are common to both the transmitter and receiver sections of IC1 incidentally, and the circuit consequently has to operate with the same word format for both transmission and reception. There are separate clock inputs for the two sections of the device, and operation with a split baud rate is perfectly feasable. In this case the transmitter clock input (pin 40) is shown as connecting to the receiver clock terminal so that the transmission and reception baud rates are identical. It is unlikely that operation with different baud rates would be required in this application, but if necessary this could be achieved by feeding pin 40 from a separate 555 astable circuit.

Pin 23 of IC1 is the TBRL (transmitter buffer register load) input, and this must be pulsed low in order to transmit a byte of data. Originally I used a divider circuit to drive this from the clock signal, and cause an almost continuous stream of data to be

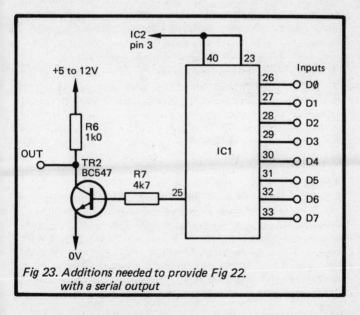

Fig 23. Additions needed to provide Fig 22. with a serial output

transmitted. However, on experimentally connecting pin 23 direct to the clock signal the result seemed to be very much the same, and so in the final design the divider circuit has been omitted and pin 23 is simply fed direct with the clock signal.

The serial output is on pin 25, but in order to drive an RS232C or RS423 input properly this signal needs to be inverted and boosted to the appropriate signal levels. This is accomplished using Tr2 as a common emitter switch. A positive supply of anything between 5 and 12 volts is needed for Tr2. Ideally Tr2 should provide a low state output voltage that is a few volts negative of the 0 volt supply rail, but this would slightly complicate the output driver circuit. Providing a negative supply for the circuit might also prove to be something of a problem since not all computers have a suitable supply output, and there may be no other suitable power source in the system either. It is possible to generate a negative supply from a positive supply, but in the vast majority of cases it is possible to drive an RS232C or RS423 input from ordinary logic levels without any major problems, and that is the method used here. I have yet to come across a serial interface where this does not work properly, but in the interest of good reliability it is advisable not to use very long connecting cables or high baud rates (300 baud and a cable length of up to about 5 metres should be perfectly satisfactory).

Additional Components for Serial Encoding (Fig. 23).
Resistors, all ¼ watt 5% carbon film

| R6 | 1k |
| R7 | 4k7 |

Semiconductor

| Tr2 | BC547 |

Testing
Connection of the circuit to the serial interface of the computer is very easy as only two or three interconnections are required. If only the receiver circuit is being used, the ground terminal of the interface connects to the ground terminal of the computer's serial port, and the data output of this port connects to the input of the interface. If both the transmitter and receiver sections are being used, then a third lead is needed, and this connects the data input of the serial port to the output of the interface.

As a quick check of the interface try sending some values to it and checking the states on the eight outputs. Some good values for test purposes are 0, 255, 15, 240, 85, and 170 (which respectively represent 00000000, 11111111, 00001111, 11110000, 01010101, and 10101010 in binary). To check the transmitter, try wiring the inputs to the appropiate supply rails in order to set up some of these binary patterns and then read the incoming data to check that the right values are being received. Of course, VR1 must be given a suitable setting if the unit is to function properly, and in the absence of a suitable frequency meter this can simply be tried at various settings until one that gives correct operation of the system is found.

A point to watch when using the transmitter section is the possibility or reading old data. This can occur due to the system of buffering used on many serial interfaces. What happens here is that the decoded data is fed into a buffer, and it is stored here while the next byte is received and decoded. With many serial interfaces the new byte of data is not transferred to the output buffer register until the contents of this register have been read. Meanwhile, if a third byte of data starts to be received, this is decoded and fed into the receiving register, replacing the second byte of data currently held there. This process continues indefinitely with bytes of data being lost and old data being left in the output buffer register.

In practice the only importance of this is that old data will be read from the interface if it is only read fairly infrequently. There is an easy way around this problem though, and it is merely necessary to take two readings and discard the first of these (which will be the old reading). The second reading should then always be a recent and meaningful one.

Chapter 2

SENSING

Using the circuits described in Chapter 1 it is possible to control electric motors in various ways, and by applying the circuits properly it is possible to control quite complex and sophisticated robots, but used in isolation there is a limit to the number of applications that can be undertaken successfully with these circuits. It is quite easy to produce a simple "buggy" type robot along the lines outlined in Figure 24, and then to provide manual control of this via the computer's keyboard. The arrangement shown in Figure 24 is a commonly used one, with a separate motor driving each rear wheel (usually via high reduction gearing) and the front wheel or wheels being allowed to rotate freely with no drive to these.

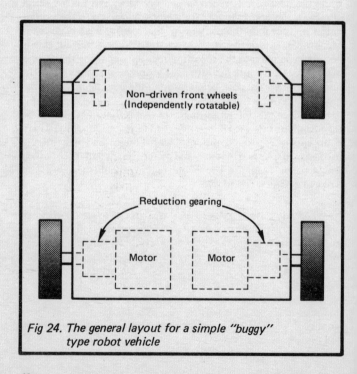

Fig 24. The general layout for a simple "buggy" type robot vehicle

The advantage of a system such as this is that it is mechanically quite simple but it nevertheless gives quite precise control over the vehicle, and things are reasonably straightforward from the software point of view. The basic method of control is to run both motors forwards or both motors backwards to give forward and reverse movement, or just one motor can be run in order to turn the unit. An alternative method of turning the unit is to run both motors simultaneously but in opposite directions. This second method generally gives slightly more precise control with tighter cornering. In fact the vehicle should be able to do a complete 360 degree turn it little more than its own length.

As an example of how things might be arranged, we will assume that the two motors are controlled in this fashion:-

Output line	Low	High
PB0	Left On	Left Off
PB1	Right On	Right Off
PB2	Left Forward	Left Backwards
PB3	Right Forward	Right Backwards

With turning being accomplished by running the two motors in opposite directions, the following numbers would have to be sent to the user port to give the various control options:-

Function	Decimal number	Binary number
Stop	3	0011
Forwards	0	0000
Backwards	12	1100
Turn Left	4	0100
Turn Right	8	1000

When programming any robot it is advisable to make up a chart of this type which covers all the possible options. This saves a lot of wasted time with values being repeatedly recalculated, and probably decreases the risk of errors as well. Although a value of 3 is specified for the "Stop" option, there are actually four values which give this result as the setting of the direction control bits is obviously unimportant with both motors switched off. It does not matter which of these values is used, but to avoid possible confusion when writting and debugging software it is advisable to always use the same value.

For manual control of the robot the obvious way of tackling

things is to use the cursor keys for control purposes. It would then be necessary to read the keyboard, and output the appropriate value to the robot for any key that was depressed (e.g. output 0 if the "up" cursor key is operated). A value of 3 would be sent to the robot if none of the cursor keys were operated. An alternative would be to use a joystick, and with the switch type this would just be a matter of repeatedly reading the joystick and converting returned values into the corresponding control value for the robot, and sending it to the user port (or whatever). There is more than one way of achieving the conversion, but with only a few options a series of IF....THEN statements is probably as good as any (i.e. IF the returned value=A THEN output value B, IF the returned value C then output value D, and so on). A GOTO or other form of loop is used to repeat this procedure indefinitely.

If you start with something simple such as the standard "buggy" type robot, writing software to control it should not be too difficult for even a software writer of very limited experience. Having mastered something relatively easy it should then be quite straightforward to progress through more complex designs and driving software. With something like this it is much better to take things one step at a time and progress steadily and surely rather than jump in at the deep end and possibly give up in frustration when things can not be brought fully under control.

Basic Sensors

It is certainly possible to have fun experimenting with basic (manually controlled) robots, but they have limited practical application and educational value, and do not really have lasting play value either. With a computer controlling things it is possible to teach the robot to do simple tasks by recording control sequences in the computer's memory and then playing them back as required. This can either be done in real-time, where a human operator takes the robot through the required set of movements and the computer records what is being done, or the step-time approach can be used. With the latter a series of commands are entered into the computer in the form of do this for so many seconds, then do that for so many seconds, and so on.

Sooner or later you will almost certainly want to progress to partial or even fully automatic control where the robot has apparent intelligence. Whether or not the types of thing that robots can do could really be described accurately as intelligence is debatable, and decidedly dubious, but they can be made to take simple decisions so that the need for full manual or preprogrammed control is avoided. This represents a definite step forward and makes things very much more interesting and challenging.

In order to make decisions the robot must provide the controlling software with some information on which it can base its decisions, and to do this it must be equipped with one or more sensors. These can vary in complexity from simple mechanical switches to such things as high resolution vision systems. For most purposes quite simple sensors are perfectly adequate, and we will now consider the operation and use of a number of these.

The most simple type of sensor is a microswitch. The exact physical form these take varies from one type to another, but the general scheme of things is to have a small bar or plate which closes a couple of switch contacts when it is depressed. The bar or plate is sprung so that it returns to its original position and breaks the path of conduction through the contacts upon release. Although described here as a simple on/off type switch, microswitches can have more complex contact arrangements, but most types are simple single pole on/off or changeover types, and this is really all that is needed for our present purposes.

In order to drive a digital input a microswitch should be connected in one of the arrangements shown in Figure 25. The difference between the two methods of connection is that in (a)

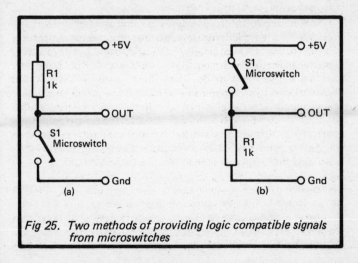

Fig 25. *Two methods of providing logic compatible signals from microswitches*

the output is normally high and it is taken low when S1 (the microswitch) closes, whereas in (b) the output is normally low and is taken high when the microswitch is closed. In practice it does not normally matter which method of connection is used provided the software is designed to match whichever is chosen. The exception is when a standard TTL device is being driven (i.e. a 74** series device and not one from the 74LS** family or some other improved TTL family). With standard TTL devices the arrangement of Figure 25(a) is preferable as this will give more reliable operation. With the circuit of Figure 25(b) there is a strong possibility that R1 will fail to pull the input fully to the low state, giving a malfunction. This could be overcome by making R1 much lower in value (about 270 ohms), but this would be undesirable as it would give a rather high current consumption and it is much better to simply use the alternative arrangement of Figure 25(a).

There are various ways of using microswitches, but their main application in robotics is as touch sensors. The most common application is almost certainly in mobile robots to act as collision detectors. In particular, a microswitch can be positioned at the front of a robot in such a way that it is activated in the event of the robot running into something. A software loop can be used to regularly and quite frequently read the switch, and take the appropriate action if it is activated. This need not be simply stopping the robot, and it could be made to turn the robot through (say) 90 degrees and then send it forwards again.

Another use for microswitches is in robot arms, in the clasper section of the unit. Getting the clasper to take hold of any resonably shaped object is not likely to be too difficult, but it is usually imperative for the controlling device to know when it has achieved a reasonably firm grip on the object. If the controller should try to tighten the clasper beyond this point there is a real danger of damaging the object, the clasper, or both. A microswitch can be positioned where it will be forced closed as the clasper grips the object to be picked up, indicating to the controlling device that the object has been grasped. Software is used to detect this, halt the closing of the clasper, and then move on to the next task.

Tilt Switch

A tilt switch is another simple mechanical sensor, and it is also known as a mercury switch. The purpose of a device of this type is to detect when the robot, or more probably part of a robot such as an arm, has tilted by more than a certain number of degrees. A tilt

66

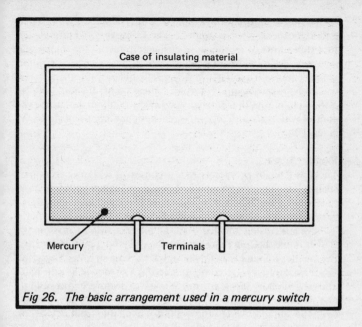

Fig 26. The basic arrangement used in a mercury switch

switch is very simple in the way that it operates, and it almost certainly represents the most simple type of switch ever devised. Figure 26 shows the basic make up of one of these switches.

The container is made from an insulating material, or at least the base section of it must be. This is fitted with two metal terminals on the interior of the device, but these are taken through to soldertags of pins on the exterior of the unit. The casing contains a small amount of mercury, but it is mainly filled with air. As things stand, the mercury is at the bottom of the unit and being a metal it provides an electrical contact between the two terminals. However, if the switch is slowly totated, a point will be reached where the mercury loses contact with one of the terminals, breaking the electrical contact between the two terminals.

A mercury switch is interfaced to a digital input in exactly the same way as a microswitch. The main application of these devices is to give warning that a piece of equipment has toppled over, or in a robotics application it would perhaps be better to fit them in such a way as to give warning that a critical point is being reached and that catastrophe is imminent. The software could then switch to a subroutine or a procedure designed to avoid the impending disaster. An obvious application for a mercury switch is in conjunction with a robot arm where it would become unstable if it was to be taken beyond a certain critical point. It should not be difficult to mount the switch in such a way that it makes or breaks contact when this critical point is reached, or perhaps just before it is reached.

Reading Lines
There is a slight problem when it comes to reading one sensor since it is not possible to read just one line of a port – all eight have to be read. Fortunately it is possible to process returned readings to determine the state of each individual bit, and this is normally achieved by using the logic AND process. Many versions of BASIC have this function (but not all AND functions will work in the manner we require in this case, which is the so called "bitwise" AND function), and all common microprocessors such as the 6502 and Z80 support this feature. It should therefore be possible to test the state of each line using assembly language or machine code if a suitable AND function is not available from BASIC or some other high level language.

When used with decimal numbers the bitwise AND function can seem to be a little nonsensical. As an example of what I mean, if the value returned from a port is 85, and we AND this with 15, the returned value would be 5. Looking at the decimal values there is no obvious way in which 85 and 15 can be processed to produce an answer of 5.

Looking at the numbers in their binary form is a little more enlightening, as shown here:-

```
85=01010101
15=00001111
 5=00000101
```

As you may have deduced from looking at these binary figures, the bitwise AND function compares the two numbers literally bit by bit. Where the same bit is set to 1 in both numbers this bit is set to 1 in the answer, but if it is at 0 in either or both of the numbers, then it is set to 0 in the answer. In other words, if it is set to 1 in the first number AND the second, then it is set to 1 in the answer, and it is from this that the "AND" name of the function is derived.

The point to note here is that by setting a bit to 0 in the number that the returned value is ANDed with, this bit must be set at 0 in the answer. On the other hand, setting a bit to 1 in this number results in that bit being set to the same state in the answer as it is in the value returned from the input port. In other words, by setting bits to 1 in the number with which returnd values are ANDed these bits of the port can be read, and by setting bits to 0 they can be effectively eliminated, or "masked" to use the generally accepted term for this process. Thus, if you wish to read just bit 6, the returned value would be ANDed with a masking number of 64. It is possible to read several bits at once if desired, and to read bits 0 to 2 the returned value would be ANDed with a masking number of 7 (1+2+4=7).

Opto Sensors

Optical sensors are quite common in robotics, and a typical application would be in a mobile robot of the type designed to follow a white line drawn on the ground. The idea here is to have the robot running along predetermined routes, rather like a train running along railway tracks. The advantage of the white line method is that it is obviously much easier to lay down a white line than it is to put down proper tracks. It is also much easier if it becomes necessary to do some rerouting for some reason. The disadvantage of the white line system is that there is nothing to physically keep the vehicle on course, and it has to be prevented from going "off the rails" as it were, by sensors in conjunction with suitable software routines.

What might at first seem the obvious way to track the line would be to have a single sensor aimed downwards at the line, and indicating to the control system whether or not it was above the line. This system is usable but not very efficient in practice as although it will indicate to the controller when the vehicle has gone off the track, it will not indicate in which direction it has strayed. This problem is not completely insurmountable, and the robot can be designed to first search for the line a short distance to one side, and if it fails to find it then move over to search towards the other side. This sounds fine in theory, but I have never found this system to work very convincingly in practice. It can often prove to be rather unreliable, but even if it can be made to operate infallibly there is a tendency for the robot to spend much of its time searching for the line rather than moving along it, making the system extremely slow and frustrating.

The standard improved approach is to have two sensors which are positioned on opposite sides of the line, and clear of the line. Normally neither sensor will detect the line, but if the vehicle strays off course one of the sensors will soon be above the line and will detect it. The controller can then immediately tell which way the robot has drifted as it will know which of the sensors has detected the line. If it is the right sensor that provides the signal, then the controller could correct the course of the vehicle by stopping the motor which drives the right wheel until the sensor indicates that it is clear of the line again. Similarly, if a signal is received from the left sensor which indicates that it is above the line, then the left motor should be temporarily halted. In fact the appropriate motor could be set to reverse rather than simply being halted, but this runs a risk of overshoot unless the controller and everything else in the system operates with adequate rapidity. The positioning of the sensors is not generally too critical, but they should not be mounted too close together and should be at least a few line thicknesses apart. Good results are usually obtained with the sensors a little way in front of the drive wheels.

A basic white line follower is something that does not really require the use of a micromputer as the controller, and the unit can be made to operate properly by getting the sensors to control the motors via more direct means. However, a basic white line follower of this type is very limited in what it can do, and using a microcomputer to control things gives much greater versatility. It is possible to have refinements such as branches in the lines, and with suitable software the vehicle can be made to follow the required branches. The problem with these branch lines is that the vehicle eventually reaches the point where both sensors are over lines, and the normal control system then falters with both motors switching off, or the vehicle backs off, moves forwards again, backs off again, and so on. This depends on the method of direction control that is adopted, but is not satisfactory in either case.

It is possible to overcome this problem in a simple stand- alone vehicle by adding some logic circuits, but computer control is in many ways preferable. Using a computer to control the system, once the basic line following has been achieved satisfactorily, it is quite easy to try adding a refinement such as branch lines, with the software being modified to suit any additional features. With the branch line problem one possible solution is to have the computer preprogrammed so that when it comes to a branch it turns in the required direction and moves forwards slightly, seeks out the branch line, and then follows it. Alternatively, if it is required that the vehicle should ignore the branch line, the computer would be programmed to make the robot move forwards slightly, relocate the main line again if necessary, and then continue to follow it.

There are other things which the vehicle can be made to do. An alternative to branch lines is to widen the track at certain points so that both sensors become activated. Software would detect this and then stop the vehicle and perform some task or other. In other words the line would be thickened to produce what could be termed stations on the line. It is not necessary to restrict the system to just two sensors, and further sensors could be mounted outboard of the main ones and used as part of a system of branch line or station detection, as part of speed control system, or whatever you wish. There is plenty of scope for experimentation here, and with a computer at the centre of things most refinements can be achieved with a minimal amount of extra hardware. Most of the additional work can be handled by software modifications and additions.

Sensor Circuit

An optical sensor circuit can be very simple indeed, and the circuit diagram of Figure 27 shows a the circuit of a simple but effective type.

Tr1 is the photocell, and this is a phototransistor which has a built-in lens. Although a BPY62 device is specified for the Tr1 position, the circuit seems to work perfectly well with virtually any silicon npn phototransistor that has a built-in lens, and results using a BPX25 and a TIL81 were just as good. In this circuit the collector to emitter resistance of Tr1 is used as a sort of light dependent resistance, and no connections are made to the base terminal at all. In darkness Tr1 has an extremely low level of collector – emitter leakage, like any silicon device, but if it is subjected to an increasing light level this leakage steadily increases. The device therefore provides a level of resistance which decreases with increased light level.

The collector to emitter resistance of Tr1 is connected as part of a potential divider across the supply rails, and the output of this circuit decreases as the light level to which Tr1 is subjected is

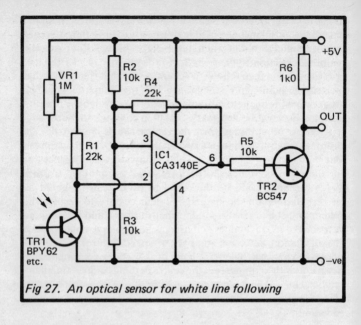

Fig 27. An optical sensor for white line following

increased. VR1 enables the sensitivity of the circuit to be adjusted over a wide range so that the output voltage can be adjusted to suit the next stage. This is a conventional operational amplifier Schmitt Trigger (inverting type) circuit, and this merely produces a high output level if the input voltage goes below a certain level, or a low output if the input voltage is taken above a certain threshold potential. The first threshold level is made substantially lower than the second one, and this introduces hysteresis to the circuit. This just means that it has a reluctance to change from one output state to the other, and the point of this is that it gives a clean output signal which is free from glitches, even if the input signal contains a fair amount of noise (which is quite likely). To minimise problems with noise pick up at the input of the circuit the lead from Tr1 to IC1 should be kept very short, or it should be a screened type (with the outer braiding carrying the 0 volt supply connection).

Tr2 is a common emitter output stage which enables the circuit to drive any normal (5 volt) logic circuit properly. It also provides an inversion of the signal, and so the output of the circuit goes high if the light level received by Tr1 is below a certain level, or low if it is above a certain level. Perhaps a better way of looking at things in this case is that the output is normally high, but it goes low if the white line is sensed.

Components for White Line Detector (Fig. 27)
Resistors, all ¼ watt 5% carbon film

R1	22k
R2	10k
R3	10k
R4	22k
R5	10k
R6	1k

Potentiometer

VR1	1M sub-min hor. preset

Semiconductors

IC1	CA3140E
Tr1	BPY62
Tr2	BC547

Miscellaneous
Circuit board, 8 pin DIL IC holder, wire, etc.

Adjustment
VR1 is simply adjusted by trial and error to find a setting that gives reliable operation of the unit. However, there are a few points which must be borne in mind when building the system or it may be found that reliable results are unobtainable.

The first and perhaps obvious point, is that the line must be reasonably well illuminated in order to enable the circuit to detect it. There is a minor complication here in that the vehicle will tend to shield the line from the ambient light, possibly making it impossible for the circuit to function properly. It might be possible to position the sensors where this problem is avoided (on stalks out in front of the unit perhaps), but probably the best way around the problem is simply to mount a torch bulb on the underside of the unit between the two sensors. It is important to avoid having much light picked up directly by the sensors, and the built-in lens of each photocell helps in this respect by giving them a fairly narrow field of view. In spite of this it might still be beneficial to use some small pieces of tubing to shield the cells from the torch bulb. Narrowing the field of view in this way might make the unit more precise and reliable in operation as well, although there is unlikely to be any lack of precision unless the robot is exceptionally small making it difficult to obtain adequate spacing of the sensors. The cells must be mounted at least a few millimetres above the ground so that the light from the bulb is able to get in underneath them and reach the white line. On the other hand, they should not be mounted much more than about ten millimetres above the ground or the sensors might then the become inefficient at detecting the line.

Some thought has to be given to the line itself, and the main point to watch here is that it gives reasonable contrast with the ground on which it is laid. The greater the contrast the better, and ideally the ground would be matt black with a brilliant white line. The circuit will readily detect a good white line on something like a mid grey background though. Although a unit of this type is generally known as a "white" line follower, the line does not actually need to be white, and the important thing is for it to contrast well with the background. Provided the software is set up for operation with this combination, a black line on a white background should be every bit as suitable.

The line thickness is another important consideration. In order for the unit to detect the line reliably it must be at least a few millimetres wide, with about 5 millimetres being the minimum that I would recommend, and around 10 millimetres being preferable. This can easily be marked with chalk or white paint.

Proximity Detector

Earlier in this chapter we considered the use of microswitches for collision detection. This method is a perfectly valid one, but is a rather crude and unsophisticated way of tackling the problem. A better system would be one that provides warning of an imminent collision so that it can be avoided, rather than one that gives warning of what has already happened.

There are numerous forms of proximity detector, although many of these do not lend themselves well (if at all) to the present application. One type that will usually provide good results is a simple optical system where a beam of light is shone ahead of the vehicle, and an optical detector picks up any light that is reflected from an object in front of and in close proximity to the robot. In this basic form it is unlikely that good results would be achieved, and the problem is simply that the ordinary ambient light tends to give false alarms to the point where the system is unusable.

Much improved results can be obtained using a system of the type shown in the block diagram of Figure 28. With this set up the beam of light is not an ordinary torch type beam, but a stream of pulses of infra-red light. This beam is generated using an ordinary infra-red LED of the type commonly used in remote control systems, driven from an oscillator which operates at a typical frequency of around 10kHz.

The receiver is slightly more complex, and it has an infra-red detector diode at the input. This has an integral filter which prevents visible light from reaching the sensor, and thereby largely eliminates problems with false alarms caused by the ambient light level. The avoidance of false alarms is also aided by the fact that the received signal is not a steady infra-red level, but pulses of infra-red. By coupling these pulses to the next stage via a capacitor the DC output level from the detector stage is blocked, and the ambient infra-red level is largely irrelevant to the operation of the circuit.

The output from the detector is unlikely to be very great, and will often be less than a millivolt. This signal is therefore amplified considerably before being fed to a rectifier and smoothing circuit. With little or no output from the photocell there will be no significant output from the smoothing circuit either. With an

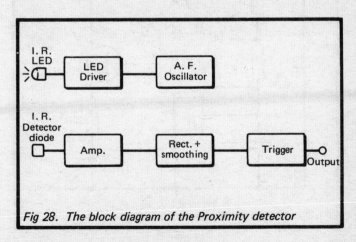

Fig 28. The block diagram of the Proximity detector

object reflecting a reasonably strong signal back to the detector there will be a strong positive bias produced by the smoothing circuit. This bias is fed to a trigger circuit that converts the voltage changes from the smoothing circuit into standard logic levels that can be fed to a computer or other digital control circuit.

Transmitter
Figure 29 shows the transmitter circuit, and this is really just a standard 555 astable circuit driving infra-red LED D1. Tr1 acts as an emitter follower output stage which drives D1 at a current of nearly 100 milliamps, but as D1 is switched off for about 50% of the time the average LED current is a safe level of only about 45 milliamps. The operating frequency of the circuit is about 10kHz.

The full circuit diagram of the receiver section of the unit appears in Figure 30. D2 is the infra-red detector diode, and in this circuit it is reversed biased by R4. Its leakage level is roughly proportional to the infra-red light level received, and the pulses of infra-red from the transmitter therefore generate small negative

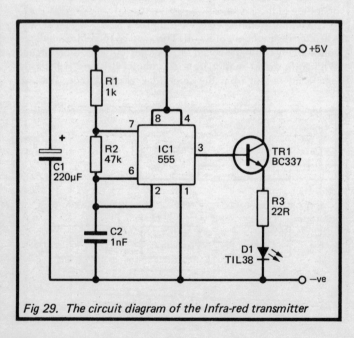

Fig 29. The circuit diagram of the Infra-red transmitter

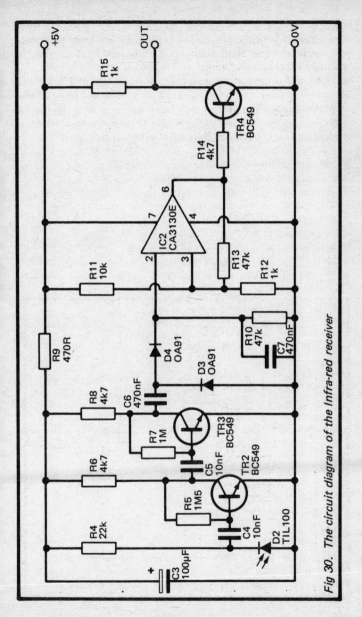

Fig 30. The circuit diagram of the Infra-red receiver

77

voltage pulses at the junction of D2 and R4. These are then amplified by Tr2 and then by Tr3, which are both high gain common emitter amplifiers. Their combined voltage gain is around 80dB (10,000 times).

C6 couples the amplified signal to a conventional rectifier and smoothing circuit based on D3 and D4. IC2 and Tr4 respectively operate as a Schmitt Trigger and output stage similar to those used in the light sensor circuit of Figure 27. The output of the circuit is normally low, and it goes high when an object is detected.

Components for Infra-Red Transmitter (Fig. 29)
Resistors, all ¼ watt 5% carbon film

R1	1k
R2	47k
R3	22R

Capacitors

C1	220µF 10V elect
C2	1nF polyester

Semiconductors

IC1	NE555
Tr1	BC337
D1	TIL38

Miscellaneous
Circuit board, 8 pin DIL IC holder, wire, etc

Components for Infra-Red Receiver (Fig. 30)
Resistors, all ¼ watt 5% carbon film

R4	22k
R5	1M5
R6	4k7
R7	1M
R8	4k7
R9	470R
R10	47k
R11	10k
R12	1k
R13	47k
R14	4k7
R15	1k

Capacitors

C3	100μF 10V elect
C4	10nF polyester
C5	10nF polyester
C6	470nF polyester
C7	470nF polyester

Semiconductors

IC2	CA3130E
Tr2	BC549
Tr3	BC549
Tr4	BC549
D2	TIL100
D3	OA91
D4	OA91

Miscellaneous

Circuit board, 8 pin DIL IC holder, wire, etc.

In Use

When constructing the unit keep in mind that Tr2 and Tr3 form a high gain amplifier which can easily become unstable unless a sensible layout is used. In particular, the input wiring should be kept as well physically separated from the output wiring as possible, and the wiring at the input should be kept as short as possible. It is possible to mount D2 some distance away from the rest of the circuit if desired, but the connecting lead to D2 would have to be a screened type. D1 and D2 should be mounted close together, and preferably with no more than a few millimetres separating them. Of course, they must be aimed in the same direction and something opaque should be used to shield D2 from any direct output that it might otherwise receive from D1. Note that D1 does not have a built-in lens, but that it does have a sensitive surface which should be aimed in the same direction as the lens of D1. This is the large side opposite the one which is printed with the type number of the device etc. The SFH205 is a suitable substitute for the TIL100 specified for D2, and with this device it is the curved surface that is the sensitive one.

IC2 is a type of CMOS integrated circuit and the normal antistatic handling precautions should therefore be observed when dealing with this device.

The unit should detect most objects of reasonable size at a range of up to around 100 millimetres. Just how effective (or otherwise) the circuit is at detecting an object depends very much on how effective that object happens to be at reflecting the infra-red pulses back to the detector. Taking the two extremes, a mirror might provide a range of half a metre or more if properly angled, but a mat black surface might not be detected at even point blank range. Most objects and surfaces fall somewhere comfortably between these two extremes, and can be detected at a range of 50 millimetres or more, but obviously a unit of this type should only be used where it will not be faced with surfaces that it could not be reasonably expected to detect. Also, it is only intended to detect objects or surfaces at short range and is unsuitable for operation over distances of more than a few tens of millimetres. It operates in a part of the light spectrum that is out of bounds to the human eye, and surfaces that are poor reflectors of visible light are not necessarily bad reflectors of infra-red. Conversely, surfaces that seem light and reflective to the human eye do not necessarily appear that way to this sensor. The only sure way to determine its efficiency at detecting a particular object is to try it and see.

Most mains lighting produces significant amounts of infra-red, and this is pulsed at 100Hz (100Hz rather than the 50Hz mains frequency as the bulb reaches peak brightness on positive and negative half cycles). Although this could potentially prevent the system from working if strong mains lighting was to reach the receiving photocell, no problem of this type was experienced when using the prototype equipment. The coupling capacitors in the receiver circuit have been given values which severely attenuate signals at 100Hz, and with this frequency at just one hundredth of the main signal frequency, this simple form of highpass filtering seems to be perfectly adequate.

Ultrasonic Detector
For most purposes an infra-red proximity detector of the type just described is perfectly adequate, but for some applications an ultrasonic detector might be preferable. An ultrasonic detector can operate using the Doppler Shift principle (as in many burglar alarms) or the echo principle, as used in the infra-red proximity detector. The Doppler Shift type of detector will only operate properly if the object to be detected is moving, or alternatively if the detector itself is moving. In a robotics application the detector would probably be moving for much of the time, and a Doppler

detector could work quite well. On the other hand, it would cease to operate at times when the robot came to a halt, and this could result in confusion unless great care was taken with the software. A simple echo type detector provides adequate performance and as it does not rely on movement it probably represents the safer option.

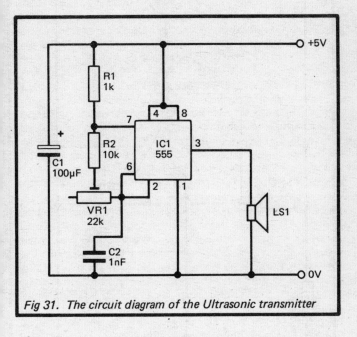

Fig 31. The circuit diagram of the Ultrasonic transmitter

Figure 31 shows the circuit diagram of the transmitter section of an ultrasonic echo detector. IC1 is a 555 astable circuit, and it differs from the infra-red transmitter in that no discrete output stage is needed as the ultrasonic transducer (LS1) does not require a very large drive current. This is because it is a Piezo electric type, rather like a crystal earpiece, and not an ordinary moving coil loudspeaker. Its peak efficiency is reached at a nominal frequency of 40kHz, and VR1 must be ajusted to give oscillation at this frequency if good results are to be obtained. Of course, 40kHz is well above the 20kHz upper limit of the audio frequency band, and there is no audible output from LS1. Incidentally, the LED in

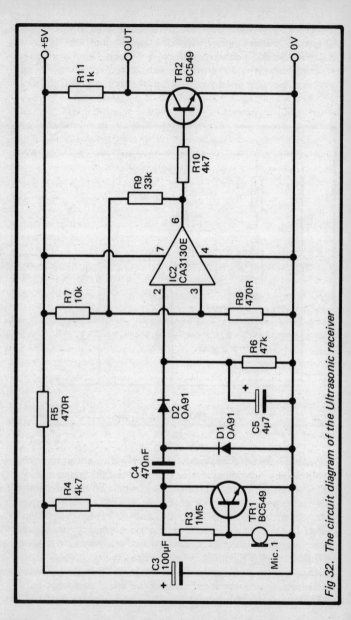

Fig 32. The circuit diagram of the Ultrasonic receiver

the infra-red proximity detector provides no significant output in the visible part of the light spectrum, and its output is therefore totally invisible to the human eye.

Turning now to the receiver circuit as shown in Figure 32, the rectifier, smoothing, trigger, and output stages are much the same as those in the infra-red detector circuit. The amplifier is also much the same, but it only has a single stage as the microphone provides a much stronger signal than the infra-red diode of Figure 30. The microphone is another Piezo electric ultrasonic transducer, and this has optimum performance at 40kHz so as to properly match the transmitting transducer.

Components for Ultrasonic Transmitter (Fig. 31)
Resistors, all ¼ watt 5% carbon film

| R1 | 1k |
| R2 | 10k |

Potentiometer

| VR1 | 22k sub-min hor. preset |

Capacitors

| C1 | 100µF 10V elect |
| C2 | 1nF polyester |

Semiconductor

| IC1 | NE555 |

Miscellaneous

| LS1 | 40kHz ultrasonic transducer |

Circuit board, wire, etc.

Components for Ultrasonic Receiver (Fig. 32)
Resistors, all ¼ watt 5%

R3	1M5
R4	4k7
R5	470R
R6	47k
R7	10k
R8	470R
R9	33k
R10	4k7
R11	1k

Capacitors

C3	100μF 10V elect
C4	470nF polyester
C5	4μ7 63V elect

Semiconductors

IC2	CA3130E
Tr1	BC549
Tr2	BC549
D1	OA91
D2	OA91

Miscellaneous

Mic1   40kHz ultrasonic transducer
Circuit board, 8 pin DIL IC holder, wire, etc.

Construction

Normally if a loudspeaker and a microphone were to be mounted only about 20 millimetres apart there would be very strong direct pick up and any echo signal would almost certainly be insignificant by comparison. Things are different at ultrasonic frequencies though, and soundwaves at these frequencies are highly directional. The unit should therefore work well with the transducers separated by a distance as short as this and both aimed in the same direction, but they should not actually be touching one another. Ultrasonic transducers are normally sold in pairs, and in some cases the two units are identical. This is not invariably the case though, and sometimes there is one unit specifically for the transmitter and the other is only intended for use in the receiver. The retailers catalogue or other literature should make it clear whether or not the two units are identical, and if they are not, which device should be used in which circuit. Often it is obvious from the type numbers on the components anyway, with markings such as R40-15 and T40-15 (which would clearly be the receiving and transmitting transducers respectively).

With much less voltage gain in the ultrasonic receiver it is far less critical from the constructional point of view than is the infra-red receiver circuit. The cable to Mic1 should still be kept short though, or a screened lead should be used here. With both the infra-red and the ultrasonic receivers there could be problems with strong noise pick up if they are mounted physically very close to an electric motor. If this is unavoidable (as will often be the case) it is preferable to mount the receiver circuits in metal boxes to provide screening. In order to avoid noise pick up through the supply lines it is advisable to power the receiver circuits from a different power source to the one used for the motors, and ideally they should not even be powered from the same supply as the computer or other control circuit (which can also generate strong electrical interference). Where the use of a separate power supply is not possible a large capacitor of around $1000\mu F$ in value connected across the receiver's supply lines will usually reduce any supply noise to an insignificant level.

Remember that IC2 is a CMOS type and to observe the necessary handling precautions. VR1 in the transmitter can be given the correct setting by using trial and error to end up at a setting which gives good results. If a suitable item of test gear is to hand (such as an AC millivoltmeter or an oscilloscope), this can be used to measure the relative signal level at the collector of Tr1, and VR1 is then adjusted to peak the signal level. Something should be used as a reflector to ensure that Mic1 picks up a reasonably strong signal from LS1 or this method of adjustment will not be possible.

A range of about 400 millimetres should be obtained from the system, but the range is to a large extent dependent on the target object. With something like a large wall a somewhat greater range may be obtained, but with something small or an object that is a poor reflector of sound the range might be more in the region of 100 to 200 millimetres. The system will detect smaller objects than one might expect, and the prototype system was, for example, found to detect the blade of a medium size screwdriver without difficulty. It would be feasable to boost the range of the system quite substantially by using a stronger transmitter signal and (or) higher gain at the receiver. However, it would probably not be worthwhile doing this as it could easily lead to problems with spurious results due to echoes from the floor and things of this nature. Also, unless the robot operates in a very large area, long range could simply result in a positive indication from the unit regardless of which direction it happened to be aimed.

Magnetic Sensor

The types of sensor we have considered so far have been concerned with the general control and manoeuvring of a robot, but sometimes a more simple type is required, and this is where it is necessary to position the robot quite accurately in relation to some other object. A typical example would be where a robot must find a power source to recharge its internal batteries, or something of this nature. One way of tackling things is to use guide rails in conjunction with microswitches on the robot to detect them, in order to home in the robot on the right place. A more sophisticated way is to use the white line follower systems and this can be used just for final guidance even if the robot is not normally guided by this method.

Regardless of what method of guidance is used, often the system will only operate properly if it has some means of determining when precise alignment has been achieved. This is something that can often be achieved by quite simple means, and something like a pair of terminals on the front of the vehicle which become short circuited by a piece of metal when alignment is correct may be adequate. More sophisticated forms of sensor will often give better results though, as well as having greater interest value, and magnetic sensors offer an interesting but effective way of tackling the problem.

The most simple type of magnetic sensor is a reed switch, and this is basically just two pieces or springy metal side by side, and usually contained in a glass encapsulation. When a magnet is brought close to the devise the two metal "reeds" become magnetised, attract one another, and come into both electrical and physical contact with one another. When the magnet is removed the two reeds become demagnetised and due to their springyness they separate, breaking electrical and physical contact again. Although there seems to be a general belief in the electronics world that bringing the pole of a magnet close to a reed switch activates it, this is not the case. It is when the two are parallel to one another that the switch is activated (the magnet should be a bar type incidentally).

Reed switches could obviously be used in simple position sensing applications, and can be interfaced to logic circuits in exactly the same way as micro and mercury switches. An alternative which is often more precise and convenient in use is provided by the semiconductor magnetic sensors which rely on the Hall Effect for their operation. A detailed description of the Hall Effect would be out of place here, but a sensor of this type is really just a bar of silicon with the supply voltage applied across the ends of the bar. This gives a potential gradient which goes from 0 volts at the bottom of the bar to the full supply voltage at the top. Electrodes are mounted either side of the bar and about half way up, and with about half the supply voltage present at both electrodes there is no significant voltage across them. Introducing a magnetic field distorts the even flow of electricity through the bars rather like a magnetic field diverting the electron beam of a cathode ray tube. This results in a voltage difference being generated between the two electrodes, and this set up is really a form of bridge circuit.

Straightforward Hall Effect sensors are available, but for our purposes a Hall Effect switch such as the TL172C is more convenient. This is an integrated circuit which incorporates the sensor plus a differential amplifier and trigger circuit so that it provides an output signal that will directly drive any normal 5 volt logic input. It is used in the manner shown in the circuit diagram of Figure 33, and all that is happening here is that the device is being fed from a 5 volt supply, and R1 acts as the load resistor for the open collector output transistor. This transistor is normally switched on, and the output of the circuit is therefore low under stand-by conditions, and it goes high in the presence of a suitable magnetic field.

Best sensitivity is achieved with the magnet applied to the flat surface of the device (which is in an ordinary TO-92 style plastic

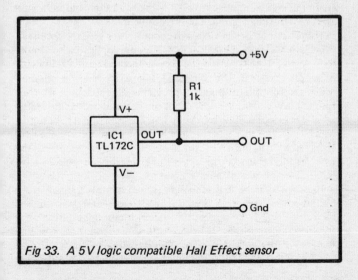

Fig 33. A 5V logic compatible Hall Effect sensor

encapsulation) since this surface is the one closest to the sensing element. It is a pole of the magnet that should be applied to the device, and note that the circuit will only be activated if the right pole is used. The right pole to use can be found by empirical means. Bar magnets sold for use with reed switches work equally well with Hall Effect sensors. The range obtained obviously depends on the power of the magnet used, but is unlikely to be more than a few millimetres. This will normally be adequate for the present application where a large range would obviously be counterproductive. The trigger stage in the TL172C has a fair amount of hysteresis, and the range at which the output triggers to the high state might only be about half the range at which it reverts to the low state again.

Opto Guidance
Simple homing systems such as the guide rails and microswitch type have definite limitations, and the main one is their operating range. In most cases it would be impractical to have large guide rails to give the system a large catch range. Also, such a system is inefficient in that the robot could spend a great deal of time wandering around looking for one of the rails to follow. You also have to be careful to arrange things so that the robot follows the guide rail inwards and does not go in the opposite direction. The guide rail system represents what is really a rather old fashioned and uninteresting approach to the problem.

There are numerous alternative methods of guidance, most of which are very expensive and not really applicable to simple robotics use. One type that can give quite good results at low cost is an optical system. The general idea here is to have the place on which the robot must home-in providing a light source which is spread fairly wide so that the robot can detect it over a fairly large area. The robot is equipped with a highly directional light sensor which enables it to locate the light source by turning until the light is detected. In its most basic form there is just a single sensor at the front of the robot, but to speed things up it is possible to have other detectors aimed in different directions.

In order to home in on the light source the robot simply turns until the front sensor picks up the light source, and then it moves forwards towards the source. If contact with the light source is lost the robot must turn slighly in each direction to locate it again, and then move forwards once more. This is really very much the same as using a single sensor white line follower system. I have not yet tried it, but it should be possible to have two light sensors aimed in slightly different directions so that they could be aimed either side of the light source, giving a system which is analogous to a twin sensor white line follower. In order to work well the sensors would have to be very directional indeed, as we shall see shortly, this is not too difficult to achieve.

Systems of this type which rely on ordinary visible light sources tend not to work very well as the light source is easily swamped by the ambient light level unless it is made very strong. Better results are normally obtained using a modulated infra-red system, as in the proximity detector system which was described earlier in this chapter. In fact the transmitter circuit (Figure 29) is perfectly suitable for this application. It will provide a reasonable strong output over an angle of about 60 degrees, which should be adequate for most purposes. It would be possible to obtain a wider angle of coverage by driving two or more LEDs (with a separate driver transistor and current limiting resistor for each one) and arranging them in an arc. However, this would spread out the light source and make the system less accurate when the robot came close to the source, although a magnetic sensor or some similar system could be used for final guidance. The use of a single diode is obviously preferable though, where it gives an adequate angle of coverage.

The infra-red receiver circuit of Figure 30 is also suitable for our present purposes, but without some modification the unit lacks the necessary directional properties. One simple way of obtaining much improved directivity is to replace the TIL100 diode with a phototransistor having a built-in lens, such as a TIL81 or a BPX25. The necessary modification is shown in Figure 34. This still gives high sensitivity over a fairly wide angle, but a piece of tubing can be used to further narrow down the field of view if necessary. Another option is to add a lens to either the TIL100 photodiode or a BPX25 or similar phototransistor. A lens of around 10 to 30 millimetres in diameter is suitable, and it should have a focal length of around 50 to 100 millimetres. It must be a plano or double convex type (not a concave lens), and it does not need to be a high quality type – an inexpensive plastic lens is perfectly adequate in this application where we are not concerned with focusing a precise image. The general scheme of things is to position the photocell at a distance behind the lens which is roughly equal to its focal length, as in Figure 35. The angle of view depends on the precise characteristics of the lens,

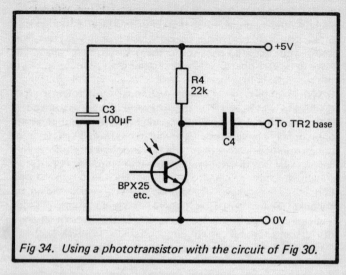

Fig 34. Using a phototransistor with the circuit of Fig 30.

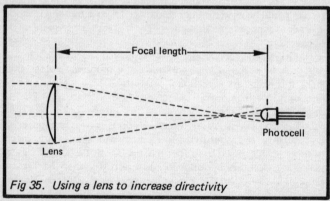

Fig 35. Using a lens to increase directivity

and on how well (or otherwise) everything is set up, but it will normally be quite narrow at only two or three degrees. This gives a high degree of precision, but only if the other hardware and the software in the system are up to the task.

The range of the system depends on the particular photocells used, and where applicable the lens as well. A range of between one and two metres will normally be achieved, but with a lens added the range would probably be boosted to several metres.

Finally
The circuits provided in this book are all quite simple, and can easily be constucted on stripboard or using any of the other standard contruction techniques. Although not very complex when taken singly, by adding together a number of the circuits, with suitable mechanics and a computer to control everything, quite a complex and sophisticated robot can be put together. However, if you are new to electronics construction, the best advice is almost certainly to start with something simple, like a buggy driven by twin motors and controlled manually via the computer. Then gradually progress with the addition of sensors, an arm, or whatever, taking things one step at a time. You are unlikely to end up with something that will do the housework and gardening for you, but you will learn a great deal and should have a lot of fun in the process.

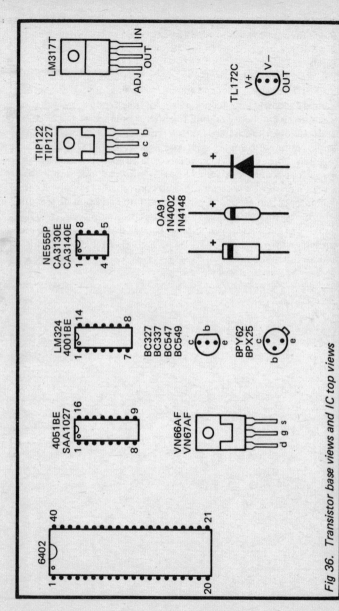

Fig 36. Transistor base views and IC top views

92